Houghton
Mifflin
Harcourt

Texas
GoMath!

Volume 1

Texas
GoMath!

Printed in the U.S.A.

ISBN 978-0-544-06175-0

8 9 10   0928   22 21 20 19 18 17

4500648922   B C D E F G

Cover Image Credits: (coyote pup) ©Grambo Photography/First Light/Getty Images; (field) ©Piotr Tomicki/Shutterstock; (lighthouse) ©Jason McCartney/Shutterstock; (truck) ©Leena Robinson/Shutterstock; (bluebonnets) ©Dorti/Shutterstock.

Dear Students and Families,

Welcome to **Texas Go Math!**, Grade K! In this exciting mathematics program, there are hands-on activities to do and real-world problems to solve. Best of all, you will write your ideas and answers right in your book. In **Texas Go Math!**, writing and drawing on the pages helps you think deeply about what you are learning, and you will really understand math!

By the way, all of the pages in your **Texas Go Math!** book are made using recycled paper. We wanted you to know that you can Go Green with **Texas Go Math!**

Sincerely,

The Authors

Made in the United States
Printed on 100% recycled paper

Texas
GoMath!

Authors

Juli K. Dixon, Ph.D.
Professor, Mathematics
  Education
University of Central Florida
Orlando, Florida

Edward B. Burger, Ph.D.
President
Southwestern University
Georgetown, Texas

Matthew R. Larson, Ph.D.
K-12 Curriculum Specialist for
  Mathematics
Lincoln Public Schools
Lincoln, Nebraska

Martha E. Sandoval-Martinez
Math Instructor
El Camino College
Torrance, California

Consultant

Valerie Johse
Math Consultant
Texas Council for Economic
  Education
Houston, Texas

Unit 1 • Number and Operations: Represent, Count, Write, and Compare Numbers to 20

Module 1 Count, Write, and Represent 1-4

Module 2 Count, Write, and Represent Numbers Through 5

Homework and Practice

Homework and TEKS Practice in every lesson.

GO DIGITAL Resources

DIGITAL RESOURCES
Go online for the Interactive Student Edition with Math on the Spot Videos. Use iTools, the Multimedia eGlossary, and more.

Look for these:

Real World

H.O.T. Problems
Higher Order Thinking

GO DIGITAL Resources

DIGITAL RESOURCES
Go online for the Interactive
Student Edition with Math
on the Spot Videos. Use
iTools, the Multimedia
eGlossary, and more.

Look for these:

Real World

H.O.T. Problems
Higher Order Thinking

Homework and Practice

Homework and TEKS Practice in every lesson.

Volume 2

Unit 2 • Number and Operations: Compose and Decompose Numbers, Add and Subtract, Coins

Module 9   Compose and Decompose Numbers Up to 5

Module 10   Compose and Decompose Numbers Up to 10

Module 11 · Addition Up to 5

Module 12 · Subtraction Within 5

Module 13 · Addition Up to 10

Module 14 · Subtraction Within 10

Look for these:

Real World

H.O.T. Problems
Higher Order Thinking

Homework and Practice

Homework and TEKS Practice in every lesson.

Module 15 Coins

Volume 2

Unit 3 • Algebraic Reasoning

Module 16 Count to 100

Look for these:

Real World

H.O.T. Problems
Higher Order Thinking

GO DIGITAL Resources

DIGITAL RESOURCES
Go online for the Interactive Student Edition with Math on the Spot Videos. Use iTools, the Multimedia eGlossary, and more.

Unit 4 • Geometry and Measurement

Look for these:

Real World

H.O.T. Problems
Higher Order Thinking

Module 17 Two-Dimensional Shapes

Homework and Practice

Homework and TEKS Practice in every lesson.

Module 18 Three-Dimensional Solids

Module 19 Measurement

GO DIGITAL Resources

DIGITAL RESOURCES
Go online for the Interactive
Student Edition with Math
on the Spot Videos. Use
iTools, the Multimedia
eGlossary, and more.

Volume 2

Unit 5 • Data Analysis

Module 20 **Data**

Volume 2

Unit 6 • Personal Financial Literacy

Module 21 **Financial Literacy**

Number and Operations

Show What You Know

Name _____

Explore Numbers 1 to 4

Same Number

1	2	3	4	5

DIRECTIONS **1.** Circle all of the sets that show the same number. **2.** Draw a line to match the number to the set.

 FAMILY NOTE: This page checks your child's understanding of important skills needed for success in Unit 1.

 GO DIGITAL Assessment Options: Soar to Success Math

Vocabulary Builder

Visualize It

Word	I Know	Sounds Familiar	I Do Not Know
one			
match			
set			
two			

Understand Vocabulary

1 2 3	 

DIRECTIONS **Visualize It** Have children fill in the chart by writing an X in the column that applies to each item.

Understand Vocabulary Tell children to draw a line that *matches* the number to the set that represents it.

• Interactive Student Edition
• Multimedia eGlossary

Margret and H.A. Rey's

Curious George®
Goes to the Farm

written by K. E. Blackwell

illustrated in the style of H.A. Rey by Mary O'Keefe Young

This Take-Home Book belongs to

_____

Reading and Writing Math

This take-home book will help you review counting to 5 and comparing how many objects are in groups using *more than*, *fewer than*, and *the same*.

MATHEMATICAL PROCESSES K.1.E, K.1.G

3

George and his friend, the man with
the yellow hat, were at a farm.
Cluck-cluck-cluck. George heard
chickens. George was curious. Were
there more red or yellow chickens?

Cock-a-doodle-doo! Now George
heard a rooster. An angry rooster!
Hurry, George, hurry.

George saw cows and goats. He was curious again. Were there fewer cows or fewer goats?

Can you help George?
Circle the group with fewer.

But oh, what happened next?

Here was an angry bull.

As fast as only a monkey can,

George climbed into an apple tree.

High in the tree, George saw apples.
Were there the same number of red
and green apples? Can you help
George? Draw lines to find out.

"George, it's time to go!" called
the man with the yellow hat.
George swung from tree to
tree, and jumped into the arms
of his friend.
Goodbye, George!

Name _____

Vocabulary Review
fewer
more
same

DIRECTIONS Look at the picture. Draw more goats. Show the same number of goats as chickens.

More or Fewer?

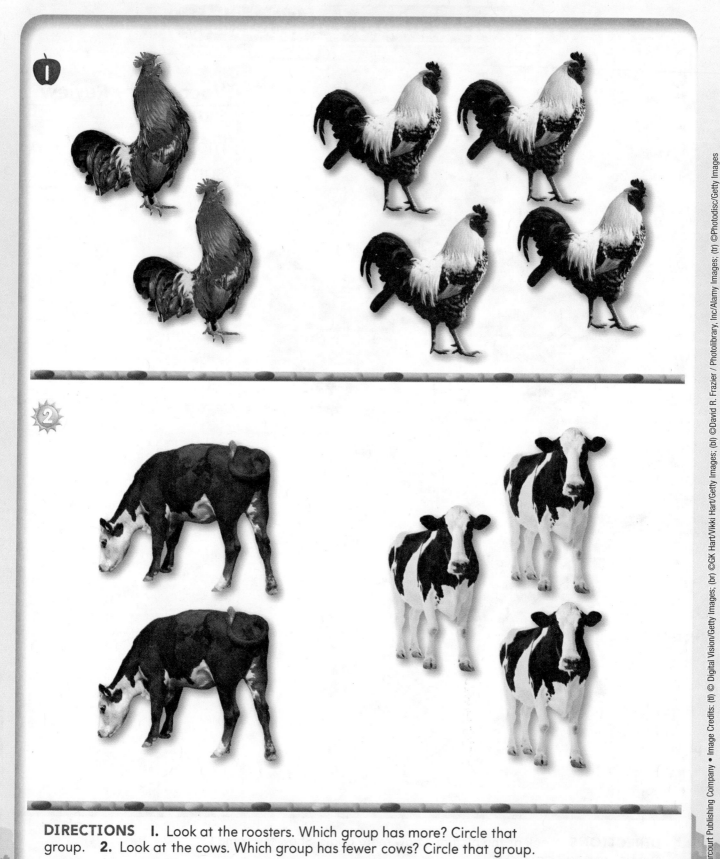

DIRECTIONS **I.** Look at the roosters. Which group has more? Circle that group. **2.** Look at the cows. Which group has fewer cows? Circle that group.

Name _____

1.1 Model and Count 1 and 2
HANDS ON

? **Essential Question** How can you show and count 1 and 2 with objects?

 **Explore** Real World

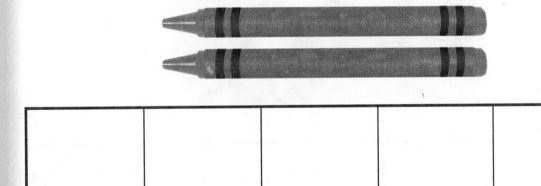

DIRECTIONS Place a counter on each object in the set as you count them. Move the counters to the five frame. Draw the counters.

Share and Show

DIRECTIONS **1–2.** Place a counter on each object in the set as you count them.
Tell how many counters. Move the counters to the five frame. Draw the counters.

14 fourteen

Name _____

3 ✓

1
one

[five frame: 5 empty boxes]

4 ✓

2
two

[five frame: 5 empty boxes]

5

1
one

[five frame: 5 empty boxes]

6

2
two

[five frame: 5 empty boxes]

DIRECTIONS 3–6. Say the number. Count out that many counters in the five frame. Draw the counters.

HOME ACTIVITY • Ask your child to show a set that has one or two objects, such as books or buttons. Have him or her point to each object as he or she counts it to find out how many objects are in the set.

Problem Solving Real World

7

Daily Assessment Task

 8

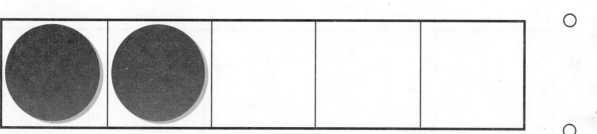

○ 1

○ 2

DIRECTIONS 7. Count the objects in each set. Circle the set that has two objects. **8.** Choose the correct answer. What number does the model show?

16 sixteen

© Houghton Mifflin Harcourt Publishing Company

TEKS Number and Operations—K.2.B
Also K.2.C
MATHEMATICAL PROCESSES K.1.E

Name _____

1.1 Model and Count 1 and 2
HANDS ON

 1

3

DIRECTIONS **1.** Count the objects in each set. Circle the set that has one object. **2.** Count the objects in each set. Circle the set that has two objects. **3.** Count the objects in each set. Circle the set that has one object.

4

2
○

I
○

5

I
○

2
○

DIRECTIONS Choose the correct answer.
4. How many bears are there? **5.** How many cats are there?

Name _____

TEKS Number and Operations—K.2.B
Also K.2.C
MATHEMATICAL PROCESSES
K.1.E

1.2 Count and Write 1 and 2

 Essential Question

How can you count and write 1 and 2 using words and numbers?

Explore

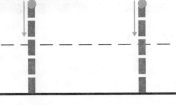

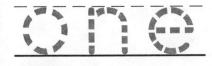

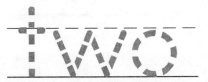

DIRECTIONS Count the cubes. Tell how many. Trace and write the numbers and words.

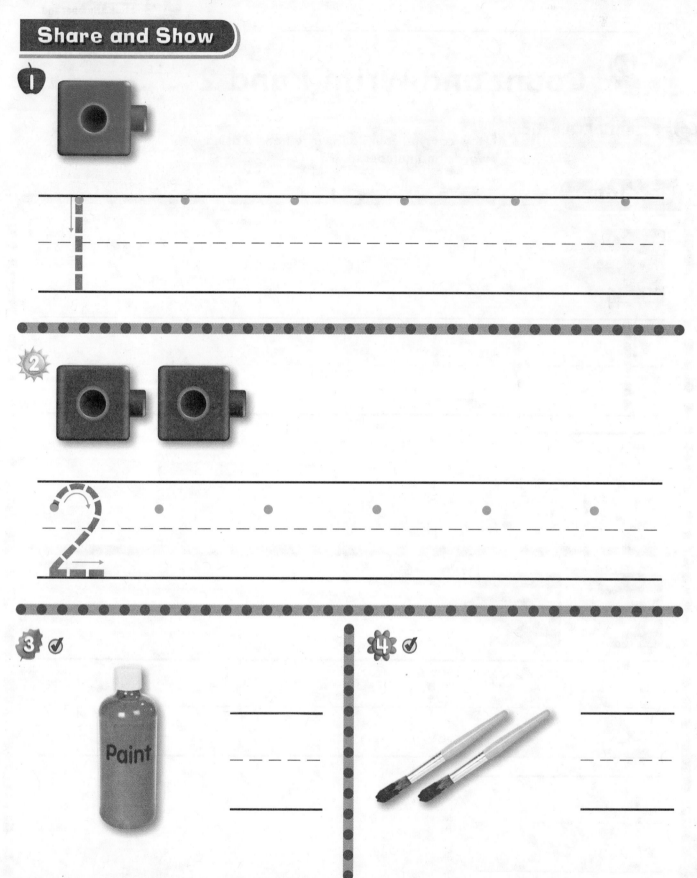

Share and Show

1

2

2

3 ✓

Paint

4 ✓

DIRECTIONS **1–2.** Count the cubes. Say the number. Practice writing the number. **3–4.** Count and tell how many. Write the number.

20 twenty

Name _____

_____

— — — — — — —

_____

_____

— — — — — — —

_____

_____

— — — — — — —

_____

_____

— — — — — — —

_____

_____

— — — — — — —

_____

_____

— — — — — — —

_____

DIRECTIONS **5–10.** Count and tell how many. Write the number.

 HOME ACTIVITY • Ask your child to write the number 1 on a paper. Then have him or her find an object that represents that number. Repeat with objects for the number 2.

Module 1 • Lesson 2

twenty-one **21**

Problem Solving

11.

_____

- - - - - - -

_____

Daily Assessment Task

12.

○ 2

○ 1

DIRECTIONS 11. Draw to show what you know about the number 1 or 2. Write the number beside your drawing. 12. Choose the correct answer. How many rockets are there?

© Houghton Mifflin Harcourt Publishing Company • Image Credits: ©US Air Force Photo

TEKS Number and Operations—K.2.B
Also K.2.C
MATHEMATICAL PROCESSES K.1.E

Name _____

1.2 Count and Write 1 and 2

_____

_____

_____

3

_____

_____

_____

4

_____

_____

_____

5

_____

_____

_____

6

_____

_____

_____

DIRECTIONS 1–6. Count and tell how many. Write the number.

Lesson Check

 Lesson Check

 **TEXAS Test Prep**

7.

- ○ 1
- ○ 2

8.

- ○ two
- ○ one

9.

- ○ 2
- ○ 1

DIRECTIONS Choose the correct answer.
7. How many hats are there? **8.** How many shoes are there? **9.** How many socks are there?

24 twenty-four

Name _____

1.3 Model, Count, and Write 3 and 4

? Essential Question

How can you show, count, and write 3 and 4 with and without objects?

Explore *Real World*

Hands On

DIRECTIONS Place a cube on each object in the set as you count them. Move the cubes to the five frame. Draw the cubes.

© Houghton Mifflin Harcourt Publishing Company

1

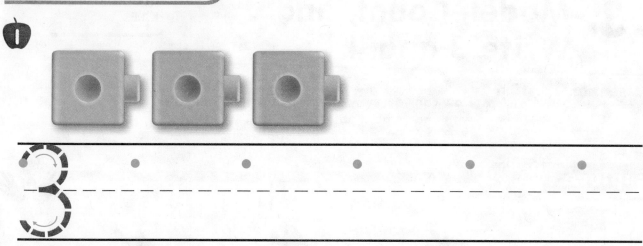

3

2

4

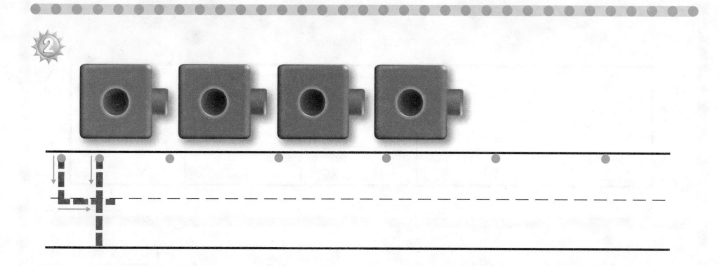

3 ✓

4 ✓

DIRECTIONS **1–2.** Count the cubes. Say the number. Practice writing the number. **3–4.** Count and tell how many. Write the number.

Name _____

 **5**

_____

- - - - - - - - - - -

_____

 **6**

_____

- - - - - - - - - - -

_____

7

_____

- - - - - - - - - - -

_____

8

_____

- - - - - - - - - - -

_____

9

_____

- - - - - - - - - - -

_____

10

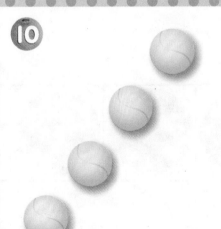

_____

- - - - - - - - - - -

_____

DIRECTIONS 5–10. Count and tell how many. Write the number.

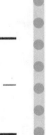 **HOME ACTIVITY** • Ask your child to show a set of three or four objects. Have him or her write the number on paper to show how many objects.

Module I • Lesson 3

twenty-seven **27**

Problem Solving

 11.

Daily Assessment Task

12.

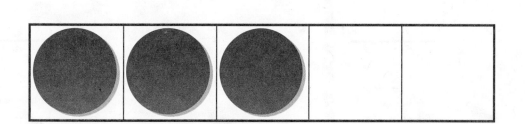

○ 2

○ 3

DIRECTIONS **11.** Count the objects in each set. Circle the set of three objects. **12.** Choose the correct answer. What number does the model show?

28 twenty-eight

Name _____

1.3 Model, Count, and Write 3 and 4

1

_____
- - - - - - -
_____

2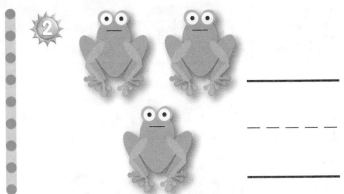

_____
- - - - - - -
_____

3

_____
- - - - - - -
_____

4

_____
- - - - - - -
_____

5

_____
- - - - - - -
_____

DIRECTIONS 1–5. Count and tell how many. Write the number.

Module 1

twenty-nine **29**

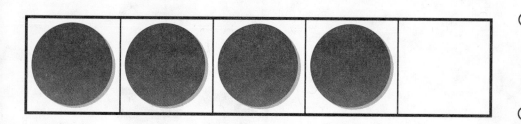

○ **3**

○ **4**

○ **2**

○ **3**

○ **4**

○ **3**

DIRECTIONS Choose the correct answer.
6. What number does the model show?
7. How many squirrels are there? **8.** How many kittens are there?

30 thirty

Name _____

 **PROBLEM SOLVING • Understand Numbers 1 Through 4**

TEKS Number and Operations—K.2.B, K.2.G Also K.2.C
MATHEMATICAL PROCESSES
K.1.A, K.1.E, K.1.G

? Essential Question   How can you solve problems using the strategy make a model?

🔑 Unlock the Problem Real World

DIRECTIONS Use counters to model this problem. There are two ducks in the pond. One more duck comes in. Count the ducks in the pond now. Write the number. Explain how you used counters to model that number.

Try Another Problem

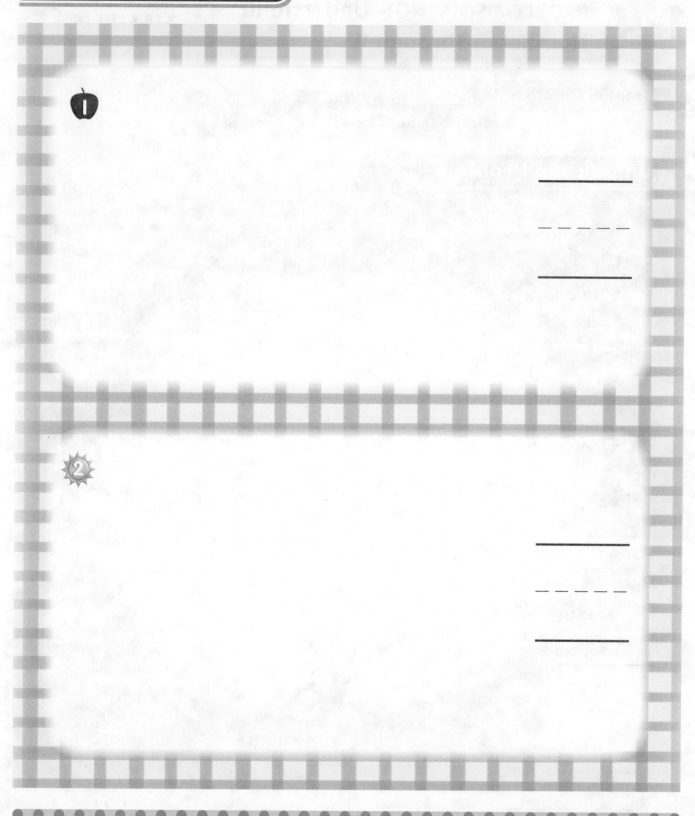

1.

_____

_ _ _ _ _ _ _

_____

2.

_____

_ _ _ _ _ _ _

_____

DIRECTIONS Use counters, or select an *i*Tool, to model the baskets. **I.** Two children each have one basket for a picnic. Draw the counters. How many baskets are there? Write the number. **2.** Four children each bring one apple for a picnic. Use counters to show the apples. Draw the counters. How many apples are there? Write the number.

Name _____

3 ✓

_____
- - - - - -
_____

4

_____
- - - - - -
_____

· ·

DIRECTIONS Use counters, or select an *i*Tool, to model and draw the problem. **3.** Gus has 3 cookies. He eats I cookie and gives I cookie to his friend. How many cookies does Gus have now? Write the number. **4.** Ella has 4 carrot sticks. She gives I away. How many carrot sticks does Ella have now? Write the number.

HOME ACTIVITY • Give your child 2 to 4 small items such as beans. Have your child count the items and tell you how many.

Module I • Lesson 4

Daily Assessment Task

5

2   3

○   ○

6

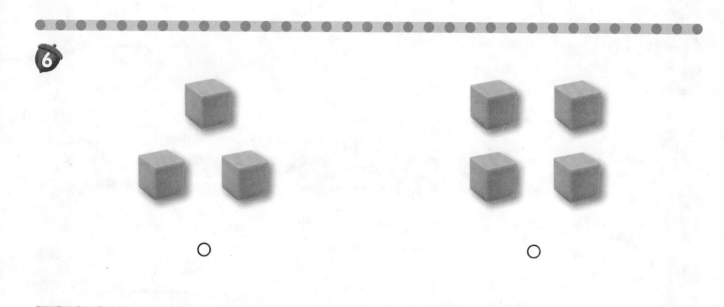

○   ○

7

○   ○

DIRECTIONS Choose the correct answer. **5.** Han has 3 books.
He gives 1 away. How many books does Han have now? **6.** Which set has
4 blocks? **7.** Which set has 3 pencils?

Name _____

1.4 PROBLEM SOLVING • Understand Numbers 1 through 4

1

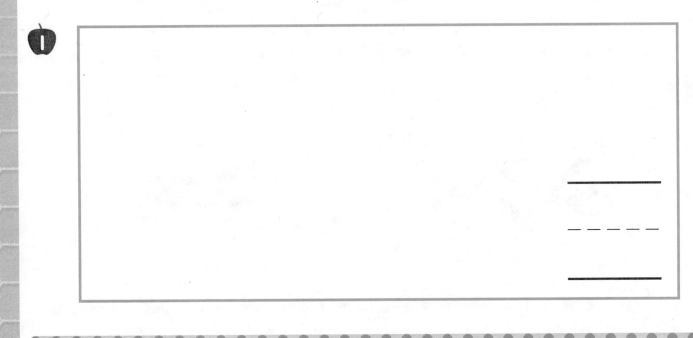

_____

- - - - - - - -

_____

2

_____

- - - - - - - -

_____

DIRECTIONS Draw counters, or select an *i*Tool, to model each problem. **1.** There are three birds in a tree. One bird flies away. How many birds are in the tree now? Write the number. **2.** John has 2 balloons. His friend gives him 2 more balloons. How many balloons does John have now? Write the number.

 3

3   4

○   ○

○   ○

○   ○

DIRECTIONS Choose the correct answer.
3. Parker has 4 hats. He gives one away. How many
hats does Parker have now? **4.** Which set has 2
butterflies? **5.** Which set has 4 fish?

Module 1 Assessment

Concepts and Skills

 1

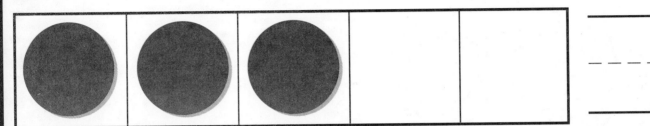
_ _ _ _ _ _

 2

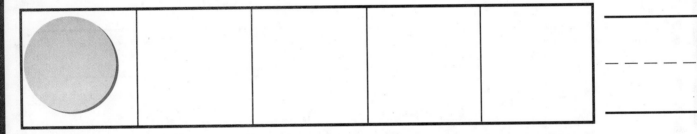
_ _ _ _ _ _

3

_____
_ _ _ _ _
_____

4

_____
_ _ _ _ _
_____

DIRECTIONS 1–4. Count how many. Write the number. ★TEKS K.2.B

5

_____
- - - - - - - -
_____

6  ⭐ **TEXAS Test Prep**

1	3
○	○

DIRECTIONS **5.** Three children each bring one book to school. Draw counters to show the books. Write the number. ✏ TEKS K.2.G **6.** Choose the correct answer. Which number shows how many books? ✏ TEKS K.2.B

38 thirty-eight

TEKS Number and Operations—K.2.B
Also K.2.C, K.2.D
MATHEMATICAL PROCESSES K.1.E

2.1 Model and Count 5
HANDS ON

? Essential Question How do you show and count 5 objects?

Explore *Real World*

DIRECTIONS Place a counter on each orange as you count them. Move the counters to the five frame. Draw the counters.

1

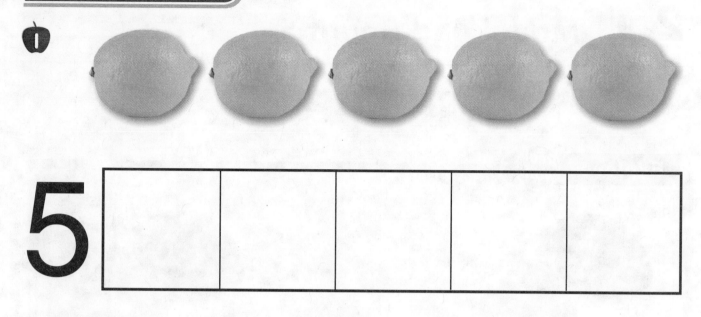

5

2

5

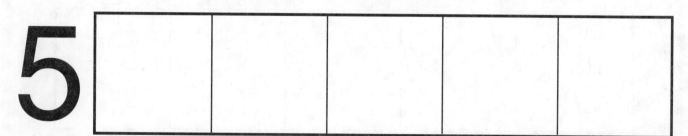

DIRECTIONS 1–2. Place a counter on each object in the set as you count them.
Move the counters to the five frame. Tell how many counters. Draw the counters.

Name _____

3

5

4 ✓

_ _ _ _ _ _ _

5

5

6

_ _ _ _ _ _ _

DIRECTIONS 3. Place counters to show five. Draw the counters. **4.** Place counters to show four. Draw the counters. Write the number. **5.** Place counters to show five. Draw the counters. **6.** Place counters to show three. Draw the counters. Write the number.

HOME ACTIVITY • Draw a five frame or use an egg carton with just five sections. Have your child show a set of five objects and place the objects in the five frame.

© Houghton Mifflin Harcourt Publishing Company

Module 2 • Lesson 1

forty-one **41**

Problem Solving

7

Daily Assessment Task

8

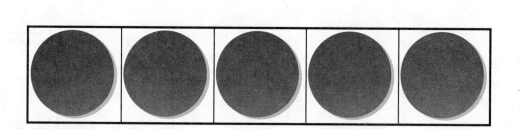

○ 4

○ 5

DIRECTIONS **7.** Count the objects in each set. Circle the sets of five objects. **8.** Choose the correct answer. What number does the five frame show?

2.1
HANDS ON

Model and Count 5

5

②

③

DIRECTIONS I. Draw counters to show five.
2. Draw counters to show 3. Write the number.
3. Draw counters to show 4. Write the number.

Module 2   forty-three **43**

4

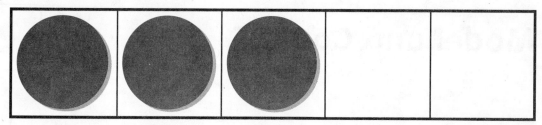

○ **3**

○ **5**

5

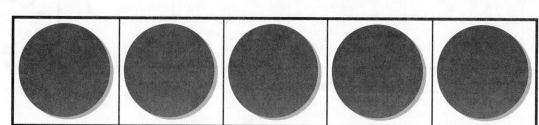

○ **5**

○ **4**

6

○ **4**

○ **5**

7

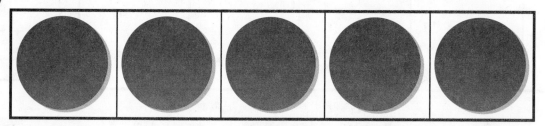

○ **5**

○ **3**

DIRECTIONS **4–7.** Choose the correct answer. What number does the five frame show?

Name _____

2.2 Count and Write 5

 Essential Question

How do you count and write 5 with words and numbers?

Explore

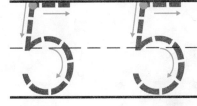

DIRECTIONS Count the cubes. Tell how many. Trace and write the numbers and the word. Count the apples. Tell how many. Write the numbers.

Share and Show

1

5
five

2

DIRECTIONS 1. Count and tell how many apples. Trace and write the numbers.
2. Circle the sets of five apples.

Name _____

 3

_____
_ _ _ _ _ _ _
_____

 4

_____
_ _ _ _ _ _ _
_____

5

_____
_ _ _ _ _ _ _
_____

6

_____
_ _ _ _ _ _ _
_____

DIRECTIONS **3–6.** Count and tell how many apples. Write the number.

 HOME ACTIVITY • Ask your child to write the number 5 on a sheet of paper. Then have him or her find objects to show that number.

Module 2 • Lesson 2

forty-seven **47**

Problem Solving

7

_____

— — — —

_____

Daily Assessment Task

8

○ **four**

○ **five**

DIRECTIONS 7. Frank found 5 rocks. Draw the rocks. Write the number. **8.** Choose the correct answer. How many seashells?

48 forty-eight

Mathematical Processes
Model • Reason • Communicate

Homework and Practice

TEKS **Number and Operations—K.2.B**
Also K.2.C, K.2.D
MATHEMATICAL PROCESSES **K.1.D, K.1.E**

Name _____

2.2 Count and Write 5

1

_____
- - - - - - - - - - - - -
_____

2

_____
- - - - - - - - - - - - -
_____

3

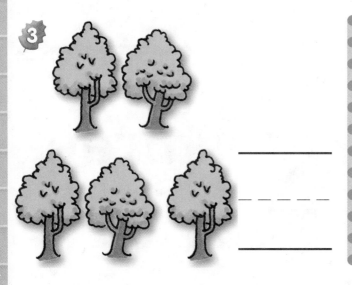

_____
- - - - - - - - - - - - -
_____

4

_____
- - - - - - - - - - - - -
_____

DIRECTIONS   1–4. Count and tell how many trees. Write the number.

Lesson Check

5

○ **5**

○ **4**

6

○ **4**

○ **5**

7

○ **three**

○ **five**

DIRECTIONS Choose the correct answer.
5. How many pelicans?   **6.** How many birds?
7. How many sailboats?

50 fifty

Name _____

2.3 Number in a Group

? Essential Question

How do you tell how many objects are in a group without counting?

Explore Real World

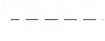

DIRECTIONS Look at the soccer balls. Trace the number.
Look at the baseballs. Write the number.

© Houghton Mifflin Harcourt Publishing Company • Image Credits: (t) ©Jules Frazier/PhotoDisc/Gettyimages; (b) ©Image Club Graphics/Eyewire/Getty Images

1

_____
- - - - -
_____

               _____
               - - - - -
               _____

2 ✓

_____
- - - - -
_____

               _____
               - - - - -
               _____

DIRECTIONS **1–2.** Look at the sets. Write the number of objects
you see in each set.

Name _____

3

_____
– – – – –
_____

4

_____
– – – – –
_____

DIRECTIONS 3. Look at each set. Circle the sets that show 4. Write the number. **4.** Look at each set. Circle the sets that show 5. Write the number.

 HOME ACTIVITY • Play a game with a dot cube. Have your child roll the dot cube and quickly tell you the number without counting.

Module 2 • Lesson 3

Problem Solving

5

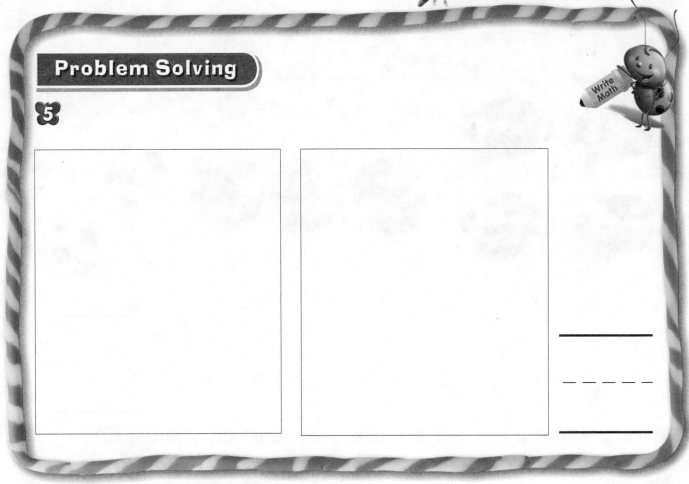

_____

_ _ _ _ _

_____

Daily Assessment Task

6

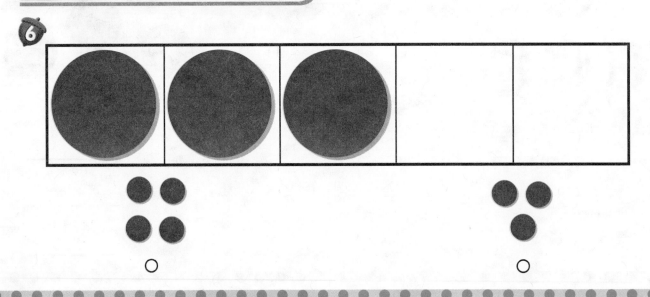

○   ○

DIRECTIONS 5. Draw a set of 5 items. Then draw another set of 5 items in a different way. Write the number on the line. **6.** Choose the correct answer. Which set shows the same number as the five frame?

TEKS Number and Operations—K.2.D
Also K.2.B
MATHEMATICAL PROCESSES K.1.E

Name _____

2.3 Number in a Group

1

_____

— — — —

_____

_____

— — — —

_____

2

_____

— — — —

_____

_____

— — — —

_____

DIRECTIONS 1–2. Look at the sets. Write the number of objects you see in each set.

Lesson Check

 TEXAS Test Prep

3

○　　　　○　　　　○

4

○　　　　○　　　　○

5

○　　　　○　　　　○

DIRECTIONS Choose the correct answer.
3. Which set shows 3 daisies?　**4.** Which set shows
5 roses?　**5.** Which set shows the same number as
the five frame?

56 fifty-six

© Houghton Mifflin Harcourt Publishing Company

TEKS Number and Operations—K.2.A
MATHEMATICAL PROCESSES
K.1.D, K.1.F

2.4 Count Forward and Backward to 5

? Essential Question How do you count forward and backward to 5?

Explore

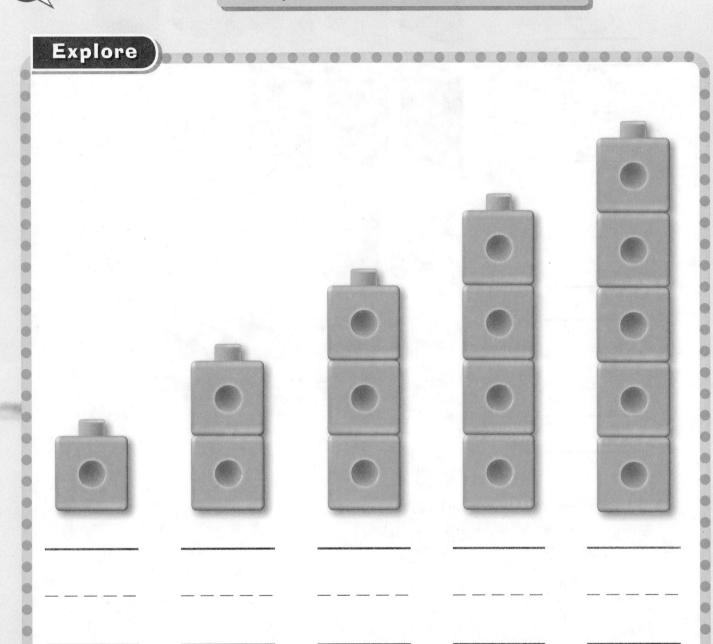

_____ _____ _____ _____ _____

- -

_____ _____ _____ _____ _____

DIRECTIONS Look at the cube towers. Count how many cubes are in each tower. Write the number.

❶ ✓

5

3

5

DIRECTIONS Look at the books. Place a counter on each book as you count. Write the number. Start with 5 and write the numbers in order as you count backward.

58 fifty-eight

Name _____

1   2

5   4

DIRECTIONS **2.** Look at the lunchboxes. Write the missing numbers in order by counting forward. **3.** Look at the backpacks. Write the missing numbers in order by counting backward.

HOME ACTIVITY • Have your child count forward to five, putting up one finger at a time. Then have him or her count backward from 5, putting down one finger at a time.

Problem Solving

 4

 2  4  3  1  5

Daily Assessment Task

5

○ 5 4 3 2 1

○ 1 2 3 4 5

DIRECTIONS **4.** Ted has 5 movie tickets. He wants to put the tickets in order. Draw the movie tickets. Label each ticket with a number so that Ted will be counting forward. **5.** Choose the correct answer. Count the cubes in each cube train. Which order do they show?

60 sixty

TEKS Number and Operations—K.2.A
MATHEMATICAL PROCESSES K.1.D, K.1.F

Name _____

2.4 Count Forward and Backward to 5

1

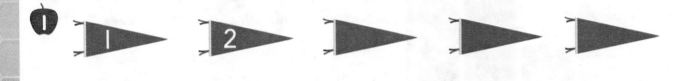

| 1 | 2 |

2

| 5 | 4 |

3

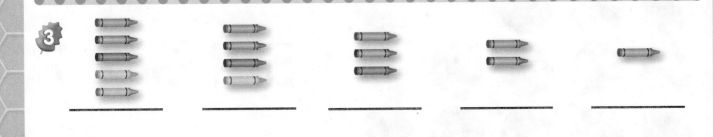

DIRECTIONS **1.** Look at the banners. Write the missing numbers in order by counting forward. **2.** Look at the books. Write the missing numbers in order by counting backward. **3.** Place crayons as shown. Write the numbers as you count backward.

○ 1 2 3 4 5

○ 5 4 3 2 1

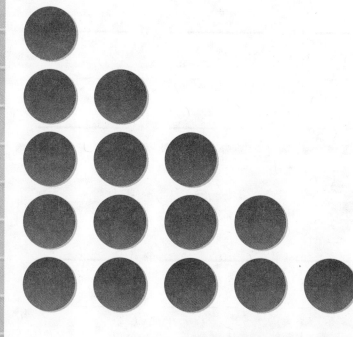

○ 1 2 3 4 5

○ 5 4 3 2 1

DIRECTIONS Choose the correct answer.
4. Count the cubes in each cube train. What order do they show? **5.** Count the counters in each column. What order do they show?

62 sixty-two

TEKS Number and Operations—K.2.B

MATHEMATICAL PROCESSES
K.1.B, K.1.C

2.5
HANDS ON

PROBLEM SOLVING • Understand, Identify, and Write 0

? **Essential Question** How do you solve problems with zero using the strategy make a model?

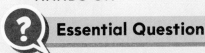 **Unlock the Problem** Real World

0

zero

DIRECTIONS Use counters to model this problem. There are two horses in the pen. Then the two horses leave the pen and go to the field. How many horses are in the pen now? Trace and practice writing the number. Trace the word. Tell a friend what you know about that number.

1

_____

- - - - - - -

_____

2 ✓

_____

- - - - - - -

_____

DIRECTIONS   1. There is one backpack on each hook. Use counters to model the backpacks. Draw the counters. How many backpacks are there? Write the number.   **2.** There is one backpack on each hook. Use counters to model a backpack on each hook. Three children each take one backpack off a hook. How many backpacks are there now? Write the number.

Share and Show

3 ____
\- \- \- \-
____

4 ____
\- \- \- \-
____

DIRECTIONS Use counters. **3.** Drew has one book. Adam has one fewer book than Drew. How many books does Adam have? Write the number. **4.** Bradley has no pencils. Matt has one more pencil than Bradley. How many pencils does Matt have? Write the number.

HOME ACTIVITY • Have your child place up to five macaroni pieces in a cup. Remove some or all of the macaroni and have him or her tell how many pieces are in the cup and write the number.

Module 2 • Lesson 5

5

○ I

○ 0

6

○   ○

7

0   2

○   ○

DIRECTIONS Choose the correct answers. **5.** How many balls are in the basket? **6.** Which basket shows 0 items? **7.** Jake has no pets. How many pets does Jake have?

Name _____

TEKS Number and Operations—K.2.B
MATHEMATICAL PROCESSES K.1.B, K.1.C

2.5
HANDS ON

PROBLEM SOLVING • Understand, Identify, and Write 0

___
- - -
___

2

___
- - -
___

DIRECTIONS Use counters. **I.** The brown nest has no eggs. The green nest has two more eggs than the brown nest. How many eggs are in the green bird nest? Write the number. **2.** Tim has five balloons. All of the balloons fly away. How many balloons does Tim have now? Write the number.

3

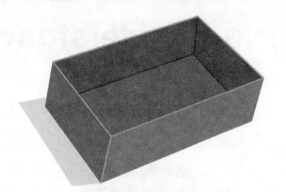

○ 2

○ 0

4

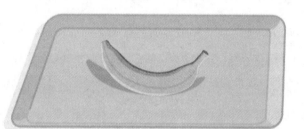

○

○

5

3

0

○

○

DIRECTIONS Choose the correct answer.
3. How many shoes are in the box? **4.** Which tray shows 0 items? **5.** Diana has no pencils. How many pencils does Diana have?

Name _____

 Module 2 Assessment

Concepts and Skills

 1

_____
- - - - - - - - - -
_____

2

_____
- - - - - - - - - -
_____

3

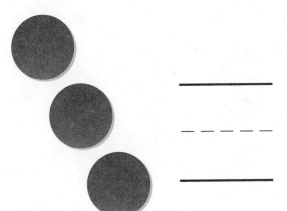

_____
- - - - - - - - - -
_____

4

_____
- - - - - - - - - -
_____

DIRECTIONS **1–2.** Write the number of counters in the five frame. ➤ TEKS K.2.B
3–4. Write the number of counters that are shown. ➤ TEKS K.2.D

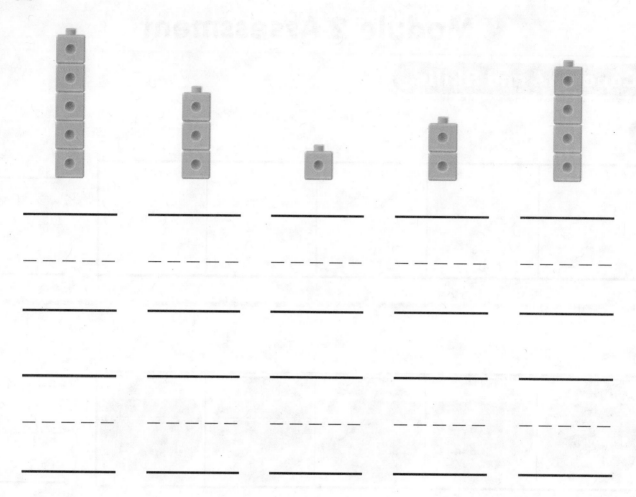

⭐ **TEXAS Test Prep**

0   2

○   ○

DIRECTIONS 5. Write how many cubes are in each tower. Write the numbers in order. ▸TEKS K.2.A **6.** Choose the correct answer. There are two apples on the table. Kia takes the two apples to school. How many apples are on the table now? ▸TEKS K.2.B

TEKS Number and
Operations—K.2.C

MATHEMATICAL PROCESSES
K.1.D

Count and Order to 5

HANDS ON

? Essential Question

How do you know which number tells you how many items are in a set when you are counting?

Explore

1   2   3   4   5

DIRECTIONS Use cubes to make cube towers that have 1 to 5 cubes. Place the cube towers in order to match the numbers 1 to 5. Draw the cube towers in order.

1

DIRECTIONS   1. Use cubes to make cube trains that have 1 to 5 cubes. Place the cube trains in order beginning with 1. Draw the cube trains and write the numbers in order. Tell a friend what you know about the numbers and the cube trains.

© Houghton Mifflin Harcourt Publishing Company

Name _____

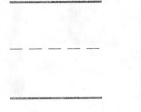

● ●

DIRECTIONS 2. Count the objects in each set. Write the number beside the set of objects. Write those numbers in order beginning with number 1.

 HOME ACTIVITY • Show your child sets of objects from 1 to 5. Have him or her place the sets in order from 1 to 5.

Problem Solving

③

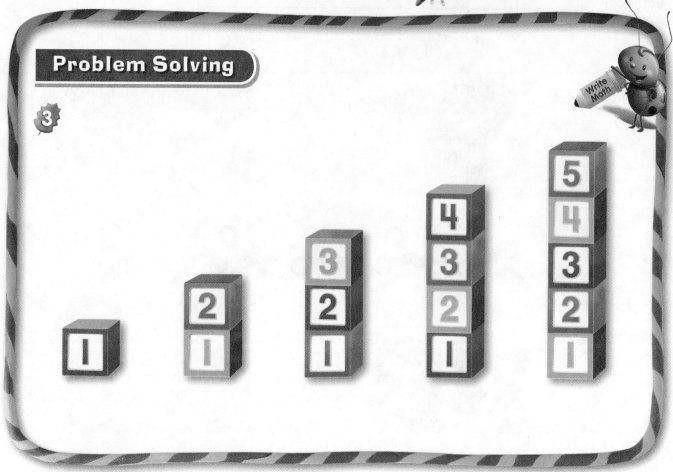

Daily Assessment Task

❀

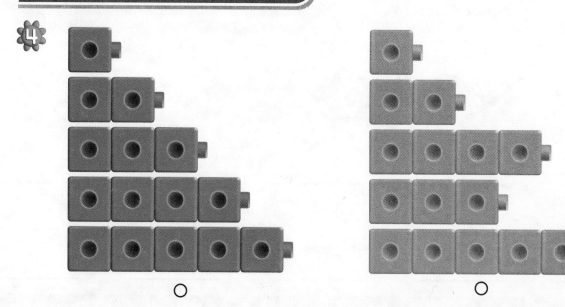

⚪   ⚪

DIRECTIONS 3. Which set of blocks shows a set that is one more than a set of 3 blocks? Circle that set of blocks. **4.** Which cube trains are in counting order? Choose the correct answer.

TEKS Number and Operations—K.2.C
MATHEMATICAL PROCESSES K.1.D

Name ____________________

3.1 Count and Order to 5

HANDS ON

1

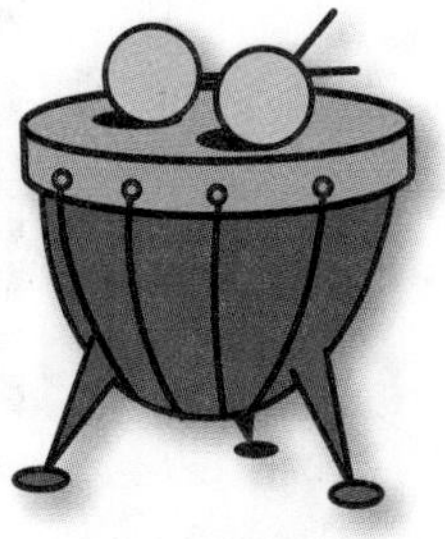

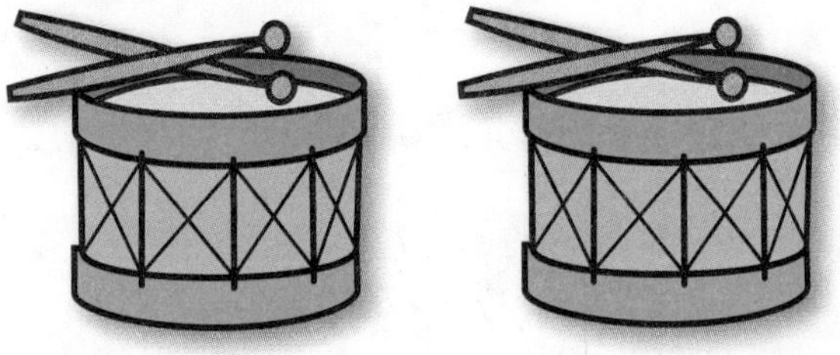

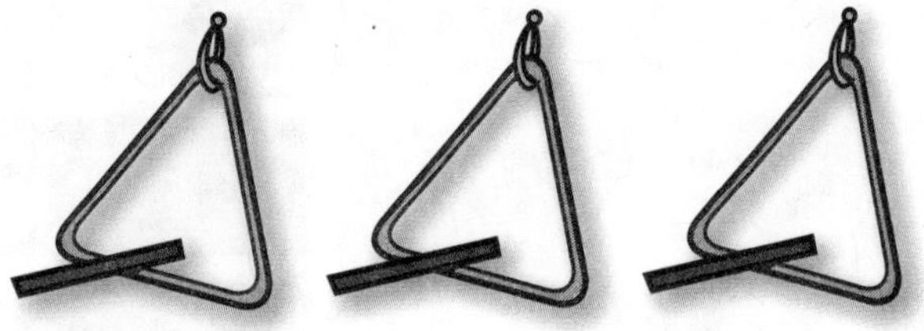

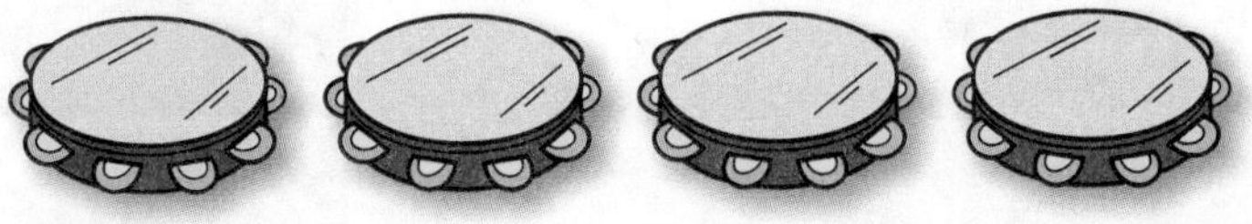

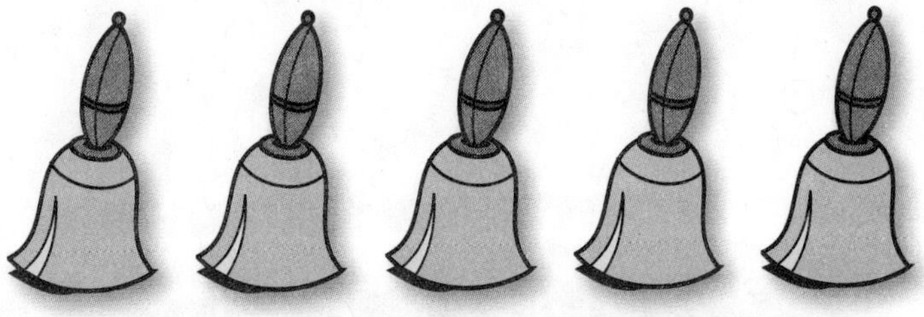

DIRECTIONS 1. Count the objects in each set. Write the number beside the set of objects.

2

○   ○

3

○   ○

DIRECTIONS Choose the correct answer.
2–3. Which cube trains are in counting order?

Name _____

TEKS Number and
Operations—K.2.G
Also K.2.A, K.2.D, K.2.E
MATHEMATICAL PROCESSES
K.1.E

3.2 Same Number

HANDS ON

 Essential Question How do you use matching and counting to compare sets with the same number of objects?

Explore

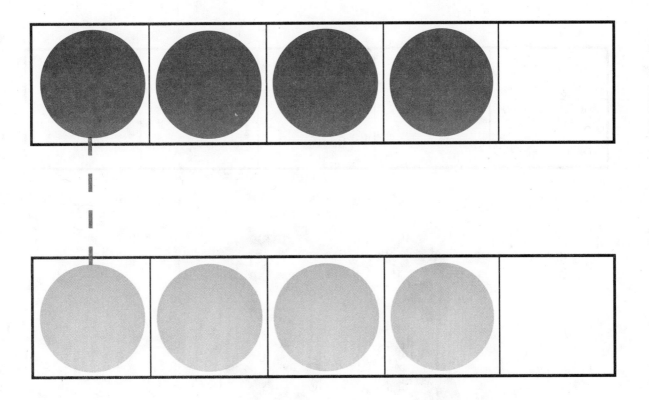

DIRECTIONS Place counters as shown. Draw a line to match each counter in the top five frame to a counter below it in the bottom five frame. Count how many in each set. Tell a friend about the number of counters in each set.

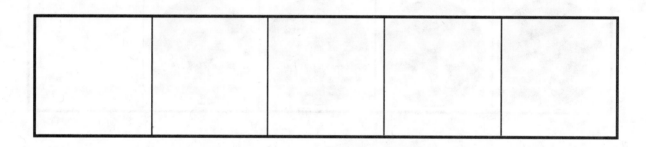

DIRECTIONS **1.** Place a counter on each car in the set as you count them. Move the counters to the five frame below the cars. Draw the counters. Place a counter on each finger puppet in the set as you count them. Move the counters to the five frame above the puppets. Draw those counters. Is the number of objects in one set the same or different than the number of objects in the other set? Draw lines to match the counters.

78 seventy-eight

Name _____

_____

- - - - - - - - - - -

_____

_____

- - - - - - - - - - -

_____

DIRECTIONS   2. Write the number of hats. Write the number of juice boxes. Is the number of hats the same or different than the number of juice boxes?

HOME ACTIVITY • Show your child two sets that have the same number of up to five objects. Have him or her identify whether the number of objects in one set is the same or different than the number of objects in the other set.

Problem Solving

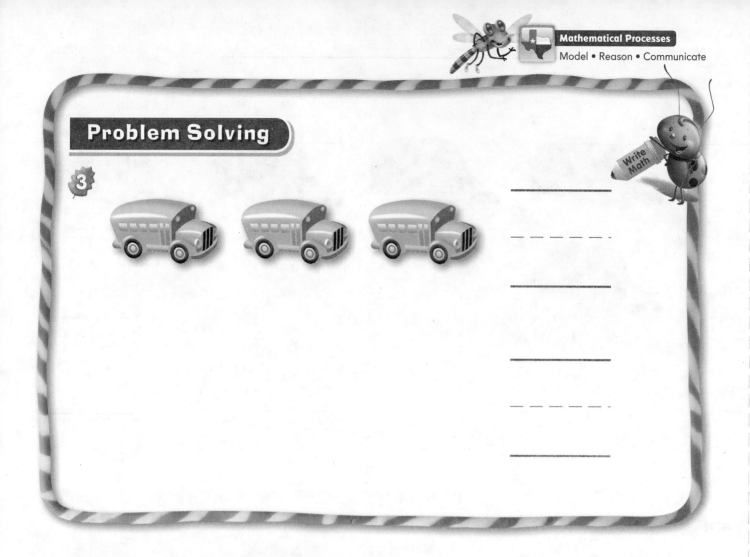

_____

_ _ _ _ _ _ _ _

_____

_____

_ _ _ _ _ _ _ _

_____

Daily Assessment Task

4

○   ○

DIRECTIONS **3.** Write the number of buses. Draw to show a set of counters that has the same number as the set of buses. Write the number. Draw a line to match the objects in each set.   **4.** Choose the correct answer. Which shows the same number?

80 eighty

Name _____

3.2 Same Number
HANDS ON

_____

- - - - - - - - -

_____

_____

- - - - - - - - -

_____

DIRECTIONS **1.** Write the number of flowers. Write the number of orange leaves. Is the number of flowers the same or different than the number of orange leaves?

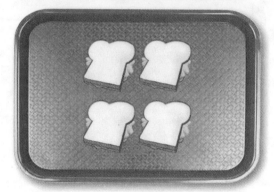

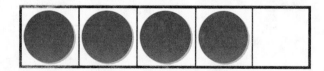

○

○

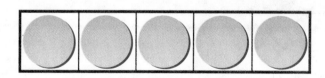

○   ○

DIRECTIONS Choose the correct answer.
2. Which shows the same number of sandwiches?
3. Which shows the same number?

Greater Than and Less Than

HANDS ON

TEKS Number and Operations—K.2.G

MATHEMATICAL PROCESSES K.1.F

? Essential Question

How do you compare sets when the number of objects in the sets is different?

Explore

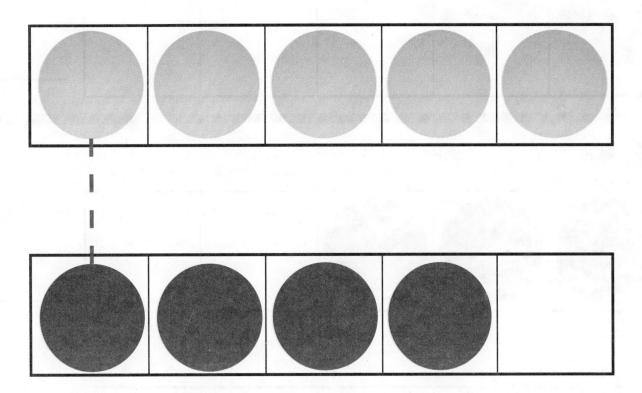

DIRECTIONS Place counters as shown. Draw a line to match a counter in the top five frame to a counter below it in the bottom five frame. Tell a friend which set has a number of objects greater than the other set.

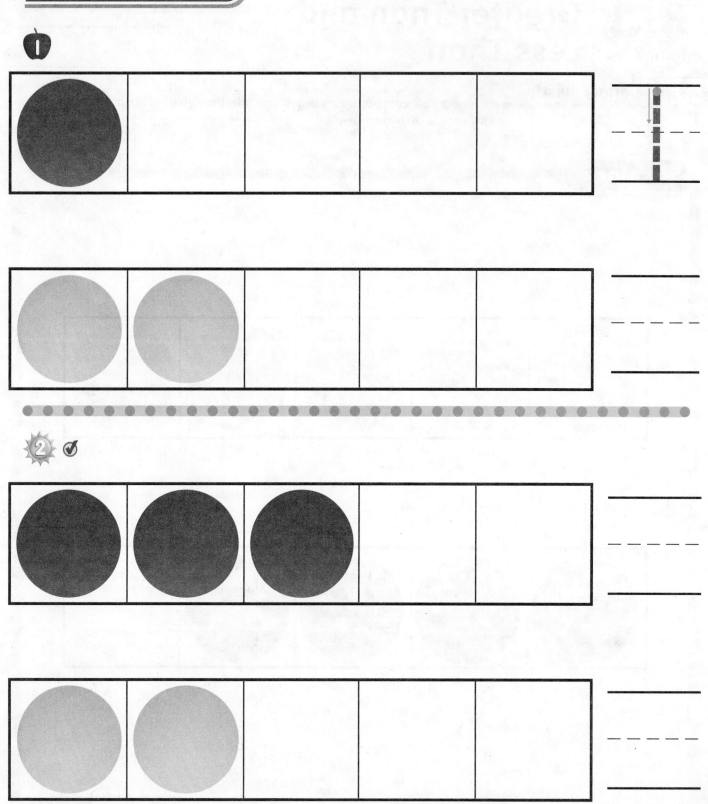

DIRECTIONS   I. Place counters as shown. Count and tell how many in each set. Write the numbers. Compare the sets by matching. Circle the number that is greater.   **2.** Place counters as shown. Count and tell how many in each set. Write the numbers. Compare the sets by matching. Circle the number that is greater.

Name _____

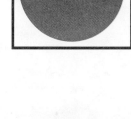

3

| ● | ● | ● | | |

_____
- - - - -
_____

| ◯ | ◯ | | | |

_____
- - - - -
_____

4

| ● | ● | ● | ● | |

_____
- - - - -
_____

| ◯ | ◯ | ◯ | ◯ | ◯ |

_____
- - - - -
_____

DIRECTIONS **3.** Place counters as shown. Count and tell how many in each set. Write the numbers. Compare the sets by matching. Circle the number that is less. **4.** Place counters as shown. Count and tell how many in each set. Write the numbers. Compare the sets by matching. Circle the number that is less.

HOME ACTIVITY • Show your child two sets with a different number of objects in each set. Have him or her use matching to compare the sets.

Mathematical Processes
Model • Reason • Communicate

Problem Solving

5

_____
- - - - - - -
_____
_____
- - - - - - -
_____

Daily Assessment Task

6

 5

○ **3**

● ●

DIRECTIONS **5.** Paige found 3 shells. Pilar found 4 shells. Use counters to show how many shells each girl found. Draw the counters. Count and tell how many in each set. Circle the number that is greater. **6.** Which number is greater than the number of trees? Choose the correct answer.

86 eighty-six

TEKS Number and Operations—K.2.G
MATHEMATICAL PROCESSES K.1.F

Name _____

3.3 Greater Than and Less Than

HANDS ON

1

_____
- - - -
_____

_____
- - - -
_____

2

_____
- - - -
_____

_____
- - - -
_____

DIRECTIONS **1.** Count and tell how many in each set. Write the numbers. Compare the sets by matching. Circle the number that is greater. **2.** Count and tell how many in each set. Write the numbers. Compare the sets by matching. Circle the number that is less.

3

○ **4**

○ **5**

4

○ **2**

○ **3**

DIRECTIONS Choose the correct answer.
3. Which number is greater than the number of sailboats? **4.** Which number is less than the number of birds?

.4 PROBLEM SOLVING • Compare by
Matching and Counting Sets to 5

 **TEKS** Number and
Operations—K.2.E
Also K.2.G
MATHEMATICAL PROCESSES
K.1.E

 Essential Question

How do you compare sets to solve problems?

Unlock the Problem Real World

_____

— — —

_____

_____

— — —

_____

DIRECTIONS These are Brandon's toy cars. How many toy cars does Brandon
have? Jay has a number of toy cars that is less than the number of toy cars
Brandon has. Use cubes to show how many toy cars Jay might have. Draw the
cubes. Write the number. Use matching or counting to compare the sets.

1

 _____

_ _ _ _ _ _

_____

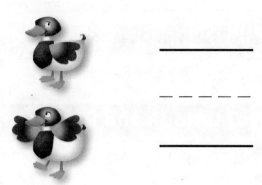 _____

_ _ _ _ _ _

_____

2

 _____

_ _ _ _ _ _

_____

 _____

_ _ _ _ _ _

_____

3 ✓

 _____

_ _ _ _ _ _

_____

 _____

_ _ _ _ _ _

_____

DIRECTIONS **1.** Count how many objects in each set. Write the numbers. Compare the numbers. Circle the number that is greater. **2–3.** Count how many objects in each set. Write the numbers. Compare the numbers. Circle the number that is less.

90 ninety

Name _____

❀ 4

_____

– – – – – – – –

_____

_____

– – – – – – – –

_____

● ●

❀ 5

_____

– – – – – – – –

_____

_____

– – – – – – – –

_____

● ●

DIRECTIONS 4. Kendall has a set of three pencils. Her friend has a set with the same number of pencils. Draw to show the sets of pencils. Compare the sets by matching. Write how many in each set. **5.** Draw two sets with different numbers of dots. Show what you know about matching to compare the two sets of dots. Write how many in each set. Circle the greater number.

HOME ACTIVITY • Show your child two sets with a different number of objects in each set. Have him or her use matching to compare the sets.

© Houghton Mifflin Harcourt Publishing Company

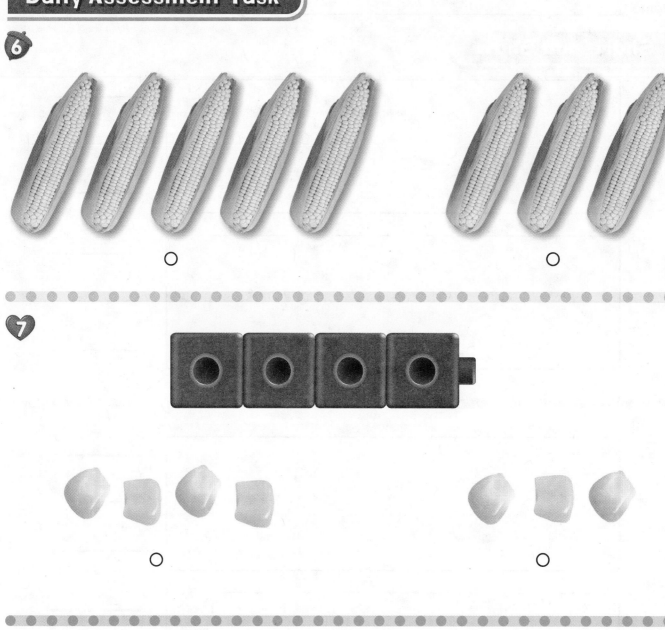

DIRECTIONS Choose the correct answer. **6.** Which set has a greater number? **7.** Which set has the same number as the cube train? **8.** Which is less than the number of cubes?

TEKS Number and Operations—K.2.E
Also K.2.G
MATHEMATICAL PROCESSES K.1.E

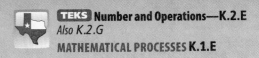

Name _____

3.4 PROBLEM SOLVING • Compare by Matching and Counting Sets to 5

1

_____

- - - -

_____

- - - -

2

_____

- - - -

_____

- - - -

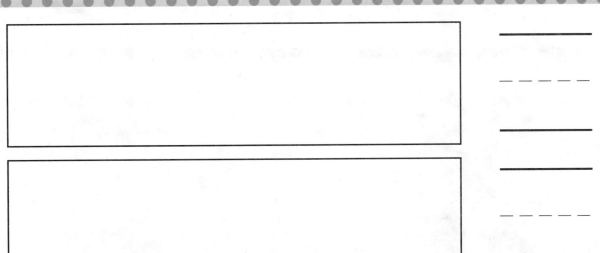

DIRECTIONS **1.** Tori has a set of 4 heart stickers. Her friend has a set with the same number of stickers. Draw to show the sets of stickers. Compare the sets by matching. Write how many in each set. **2.** Draw two sets of circles with the same number. Show what you know about matching to compare two sets of objects. Write how many in each set.

3

○ **3**

○ **4**

4

○ **2**

○ **3**

5

○

○

DIRECTIONS Choose the correct answer.
3. Which is greater than the number of cubes?
4. Which is less than the number of cubes?
5. Which set has a greater number?

94 ninety-four

Module 3 Assessment

Concepts and Skills

_____

- - - - - - - - - - - -

_____

- - - - - - - - - - - -

_____

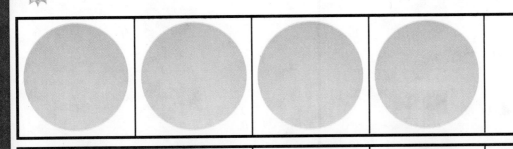

_____

- - - - - - - - - - - -

_____

- - - - - - - - - - - -

_____

DIRECTIONS **I.** Place a counter below each object to show the same number of objects. Draw and color each counter. Write how many objects in each row. ⬇TEKS K.2.G
2. Place counters as shown. Count and tell how many in each set. Write the numbers. Compare the sets by matching. Circle the number that is greater. ⬇TEKS K.2.G

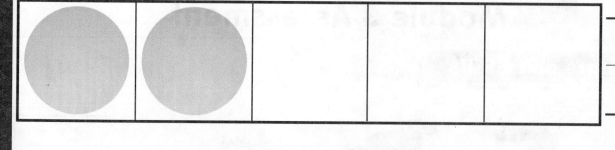

---

4 ⭐ **TEXAS Test Prep**

○   ○

DIRECTIONS 3. Count and tell how many counters are in the five frame. Make a set with more counters in the five frame below. Trace and draw the counters. Write the number. Compare the sets by matching. ◀ TEKS K.2.G **4.** Choose the correct answer. Which set has a number of animals that is greater? ◀ TEKS K.2.G

TEKS Number and Operations—K.2.B
Also K.2.C, K.2.I
MATHEMATICAL PROCESSES
K.1.A, K.1.E

4.1 Model and Count 6
HANDS ON

? **Essential Question**   How can you show and count 6 objects?

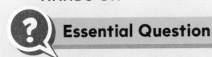

DIRECTIONS   Place a counter on each ticket in the set as you count them. Move the counters to the ten frame. Draw the counters.

6
six

DIRECTIONS 1. Place a counter on each car in the set as you count them. Move the counters to the parking lot. Draw the counters.

6
six

_____   _____

_____   _____

and

_____   _____

_____   _____

and

_____   _____

_____   _____

and

_____   _____

_____   _____

and

DIRECTIONS 2. Place two-color counters in the ten frame to model the different ways to make 6. Write to show some pairs of numbers that make 6.

HOME ACTIVITY • Ask your child to show a set of five objects. Have him or her show one more object and tell how many objects are in the set.

Module 4 • Lesson 1

Problem Solving Real World

3

Daily Assessment Task

4

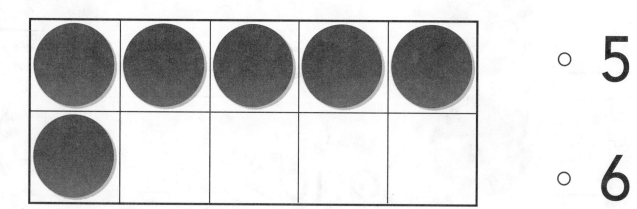

○ 5

○ 6

DIRECTIONS 3. Six people bought popcorn. Count the buckets of popcorn in each set. Circle the sets that show six buckets. **4.** Choose the correct answer. What number does the model show?

TEKS **Number and Operations—K.2.B**
Also *K.2.C, K.2.I*
MATHEMATICAL PROCESSES K.1.A, K.1.E

Name _____

4.1 Model and Count 6

HANDS ON

🍎 1

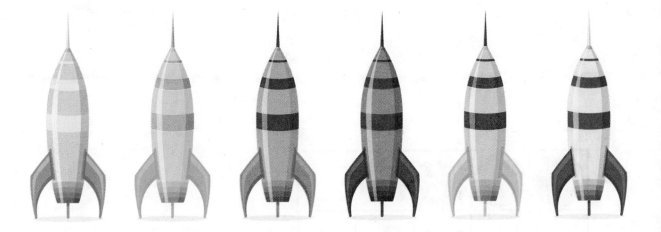

DIRECTIONS **1.** Mark an X on each rocket ship as you count them. Draw a counter on the ten frame as you count each rocket ship.

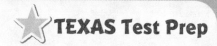

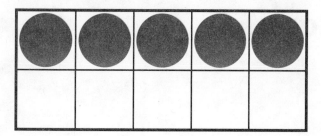

○ **5**

○ **6**

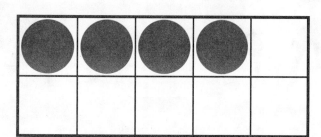

○ **6**

○ **4**

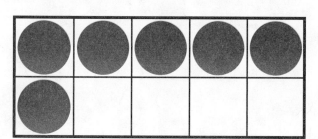

○ **6**

○ **5**

DIRECTIONS Choose the correct answer.
2–4. What number does the model show?

TEKS Number and
Operations—K.2.B
Also K.2.C
MATHEMATICAL PROCESSES
K.1.A, K.1.E

4.2 Count and Write 6

? **Essential Question**

How can you count and write 6 using words and numbers?

Explore

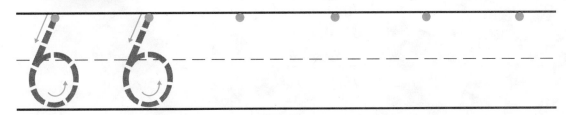

DIRECTIONS Count and tell how many cubes. Trace and write the numbers. Count and tell how many hats. Trace the word.

DIRECTIONS 1. Look at the picture. Circle the sets of six objects.

Name _____

  six

3 ✓

_____

_ _ _ _ _ _ _

_____

4 ✓

_____

_ _ _ _ _ _ _

_____

5

_____

_ _ _ _ _ _ _

_____

6

_____

_ _ _ _ _ _ _

_____

DIRECTIONS   2. Say the number. Practice writing the number.   **3–6.** Count and tell how many. Write the number.

 HOME ACTIVITY • Show six objects. Have your child point to each object as he or she counts it. Then have him or her write the number on paper to show how many.

Problem Solving Real World

7

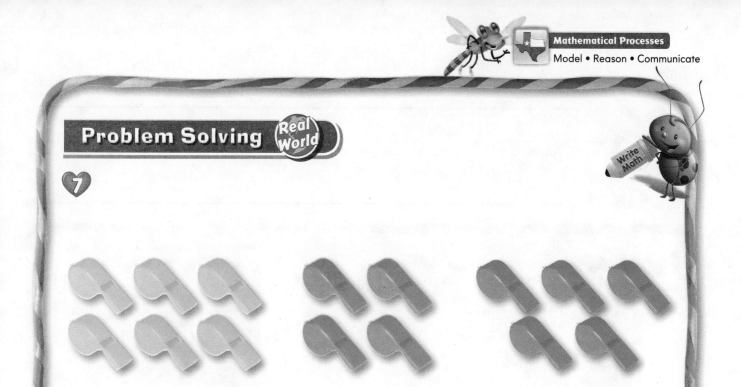

Daily Assessment Task

8

2 ○   6 ○

DIRECTIONS 7. Marta has a number of whistles that is two less than 6. Count the whistles in each set. Circle the set that shows a number of whistles that is two less than 6. **8.** Choose the correct answer. What number does the model show?

TEKS Number and Operations—K.2.B
Also K.2.C
MATHEMATICAL PROCESSES K.1.A, K.1.E

Name _____

4.2 Count and Write 6

1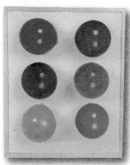

_____
- - - - - -
_____

2

_____
- - - - - -
_____

3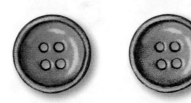

_____
- - - - - -
_____

4

_____
- - - - - -
_____

DIRECTIONS **1–4.** Count and tell how many.
Write the numbers.

5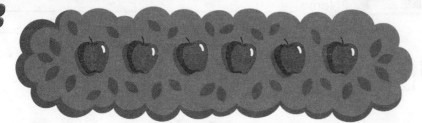

○ **6**

○ **5**

6

○ **3**

○ **6**

7

○ **six**

○ **four**

DIRECTIONS Choose the correct answer.
5–7. Count and tell how many.

108 one hundred eight

Name _____

TEKS Number and Operations—K.2.B
Also K.2.C, K.2.I
MATHEMATICAL PROCESSES
K.1.E, K.1.G

 Model and Count 7

HANDS ON

 Essential Question

How can you show and count 7 objects?

Explore

DIRECTIONS Model 6 objects. Show one more object. How many are there now? Tell a friend how you know. Draw the objects.

7

seven

5 and ___ more

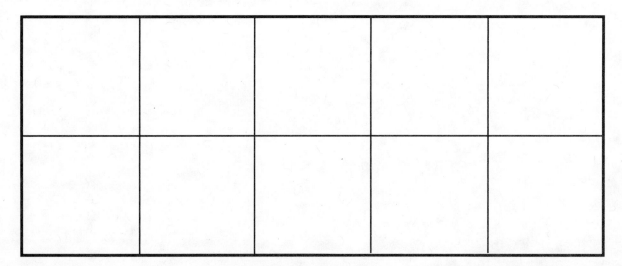

DIRECTIONS 1. Place counters as shown. Count and tell how many counters.
2. 5 and how many more are 7? Write the number.   3. Place counters in the ten frame to model seven. Draw the counters. Tell a friend what you know about the number 7.

Name _____

7
seven

_____
- - - - - -
_____   **and**

_____
- - - - - -   **and**
_____

_____
- - - - - -   **and**
_____

_____
- - - - - -   **and**
_____

_____
- - - - - -
_____

_____
- - - - - -
_____

_____
- - - - - -
_____

●●

DIRECTIONS **4.** Place two-color counters in the ten frame to model the different ways to make 7. Write to show some pairs of numbers that make 7.

HOME ACTIVITY • Ask your child to show a set of six objects. Have him or her show one more object and tell how many objects are in the set.

Module 4 • Lesson 3   one hundred eleven **111**

© Houghton Mifflin Harcourt Publishing Company

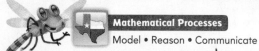
Problem Solving Real World

5

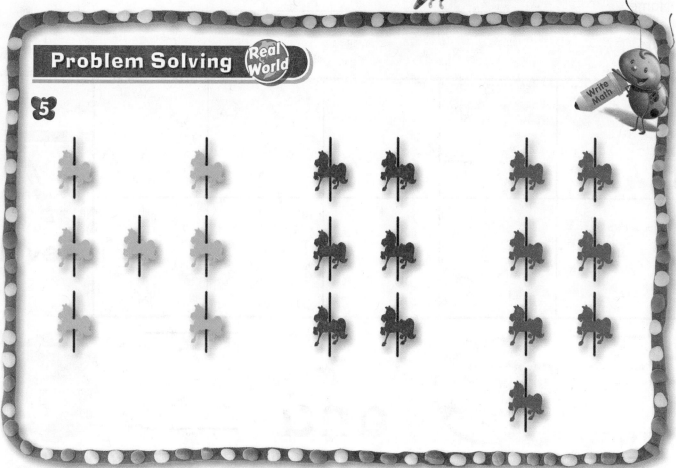

Daily Assessment Task

6

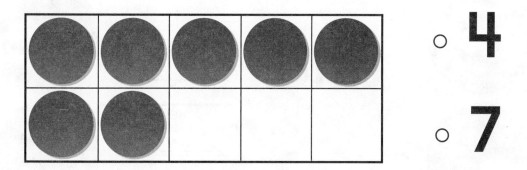

○ **4**

○ **7**

DIRECTIONS 5. A carousel needs seven horses. Count the horses in each set. Circle the sets with seven horses. **6.** Choose the correct answer. What number does the model show?

Homework and Practice

TEKS Number and Operations—K.2.B
Also K.2.C, K.2.I
MATHEMATICAL PROCESSES K.1.E, K.1.G

Name _____

4.3 Model and Count 7

HANDS ON

 1

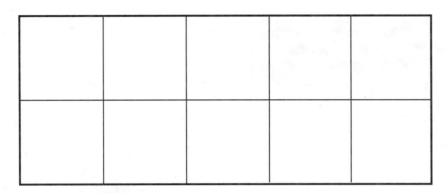

7
seven

_____  and _____

 2

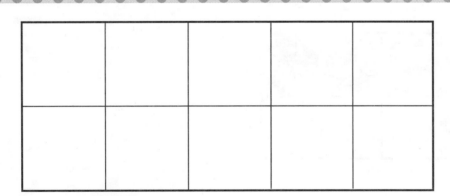

7
seven

_____  and _____

DIRECTIONS   1. Draw some red and yellow counters to make 7. Write to show the number of red and number of yellow counters.   **2.** Draw some red and yellow counters to make 7 another way. Write to show the number of red and number of yellow counters.

 ③

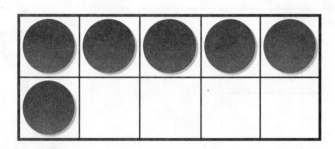

○ **6**

○ **7**

 ④

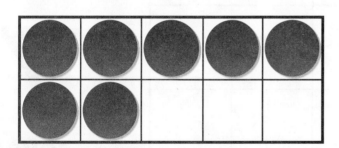

○ **7**

○ **5**

DIRECTIONS Choose the correct answer.
3–4. What number does the model show?

Name _____

4.4 Count and Write 7

? **Essential Question**
How can you count and write 7 using words and numbers?

Explore

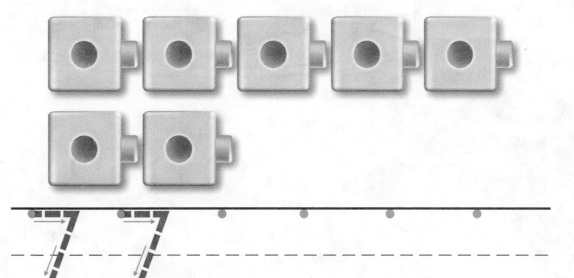

DIRECTIONS Count and tell how many cubes. Trace and write the numbers. Count and tell how many hats. Trace the word.

1

DIRECTIONS 1. Look at the picture. Circle the sets of seven objects.

Name _____

7
seven

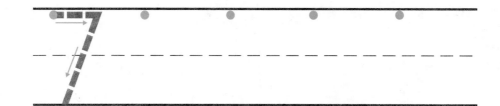

_____
- - - - - - - -
_____

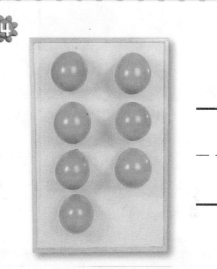

_____
- - - - - - - -
_____

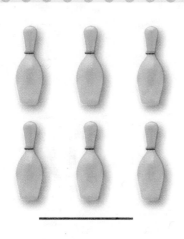

_____
- - - - - - - -
_____

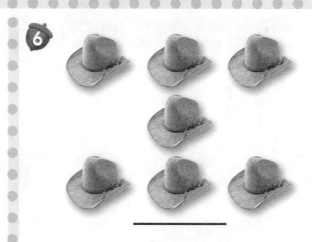

_____
- - - - - - - -
_____

DIRECTIONS **2.** Say the number. Practice writing the number. **3–6.** Count and tell how many. Write the number.

HOME ACTIVITY • Show your child seven objects. Have him or her point to each object as he or she counts it. Then have him or her write the number on paper to show how many objects.

Problem Solving Real World

7

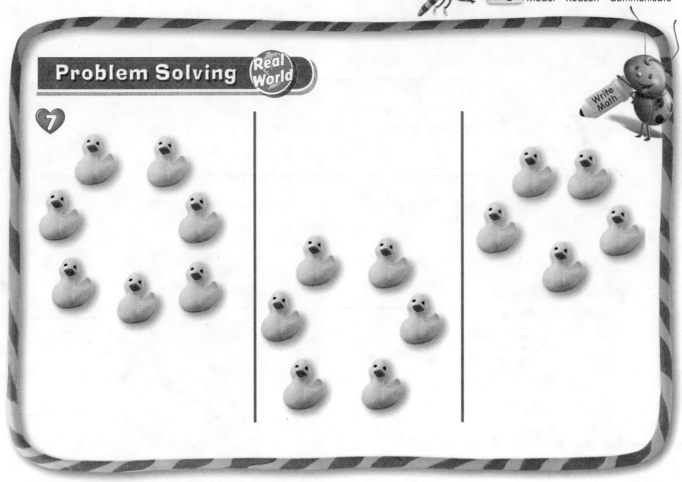

Daily Assessment Task

8

○ **six**

○ **seven**

DIRECTIONS **7.** Jason has a number of ducks that is two greater than 5. Count the ducks in each set. Circle the set that shows a number of ducks that is two greater than 5. **8.** Choose the correct answer. Which number does the model show?

Name _____

TEKS Number and Operations—K.2.B
Also K.2.C
MATHEMATICAL PROCESSES K.1.A, K.1.E

4.4 Count and Write 7

1

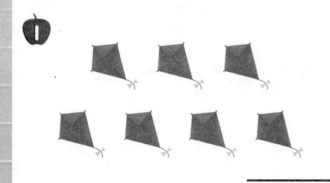

_____

- - - - - - - - -

_____

2

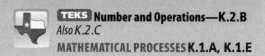

_____

- - - - - - - - -

_____

3

_____

- - - - - - - - -

_____

4

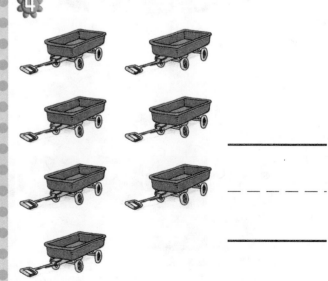

_____

- - - - - - - - -

_____

DIRECTIONS 1–4. Count and tell how many. Write the number.

5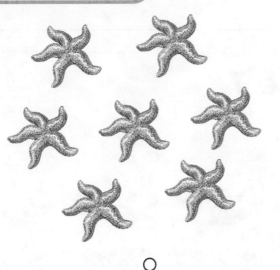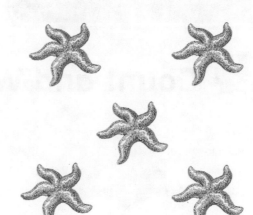

○   ○

6

○   ○

7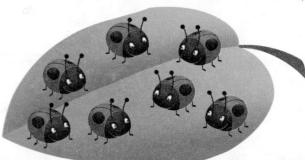

○ **seven**

○ **five**

DIRECTIONS Choose the correct answer.
5. Which set has seven starfish? **6.** Which set has seven ladybugs? **7.** Which number does the model show?

120 one hundred twenty

4.5
HANDS ON

Model, Count, and Write 8

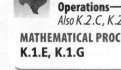

TEKS **Number and Operations—K.2.B**
Also K.2.C, K.2.E, K.2.I
MATHEMATICAL PROCESSES
K.1.E, K.1.G

? **Essential Question**

How can you show, count, and write 8 with and without objects?

Explore

DIRECTIONS Model 7 objects. Show one more object. How many objects are there now? Tell a friend how you know. Draw the objects.

1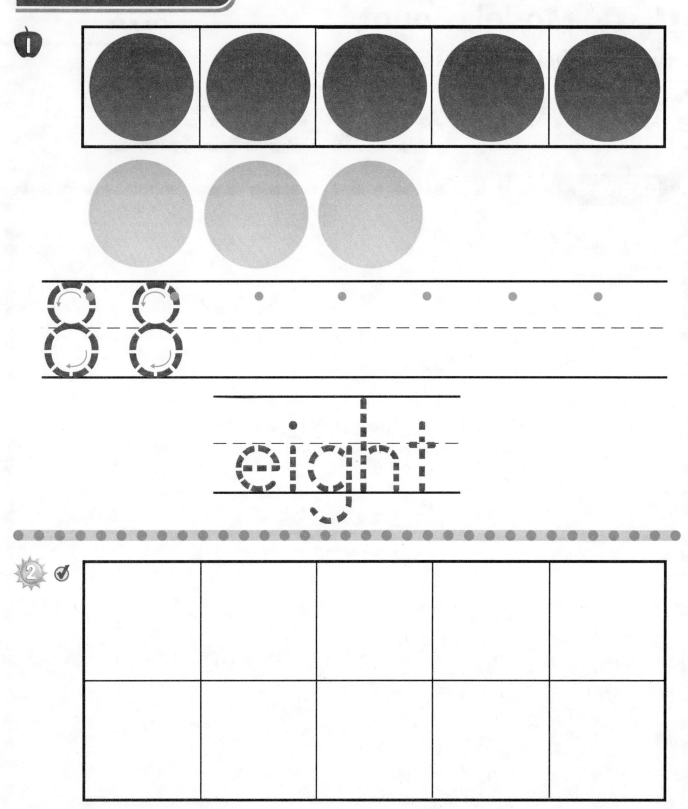

88
88

eight

2 ✓

DIRECTIONS **1.** Place counters as shown. Count and tell how many counters. Trace and write the numbers. Trace the word. **2.** Place counters in the ten frame to model eight. Draw the counters. Tell a friend what you know about the number 8.

122 one hundred twenty-two

3

_____
_ _ _ _ _
eight

_____
_ _ _ _ _
_____
_ _ _ _ _

and

and

and

and

_____
_ _ _ _ _
_____
_ _ _ _ _
_____

DIRECTIONS 3. Write the number 8. Place two-color counters in the ten frame to model the different ways to make 8. Write to show some pairs of numbers that make 8.

HOME ACTIVITY • Ask your child to show a set of seven objects. Have him or her show one more object and tell how many.

Problem Solving

4

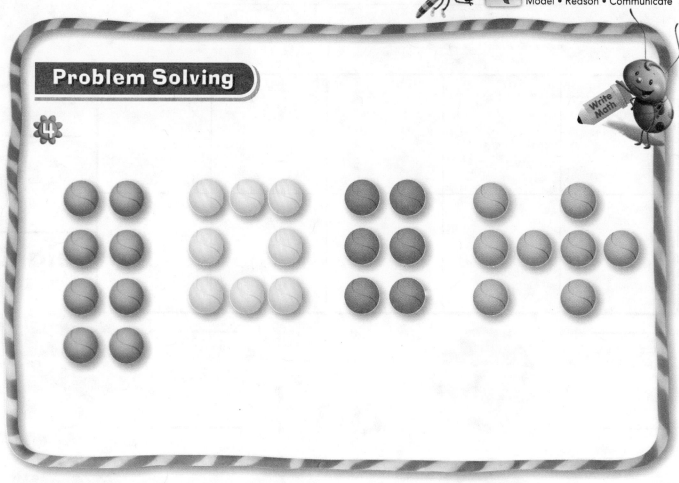

Daily Assessment Task

5

○ **6**

○ **8**

DIRECTIONS **4.** Count the balls in each set. Which sets show eight balls? Circle those sets. **5.** Choose the correct answer. How many parrots are there?

124 one hundred twenty-four

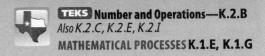

Name _____

 Model, Count, and Write 8

HANDS ON

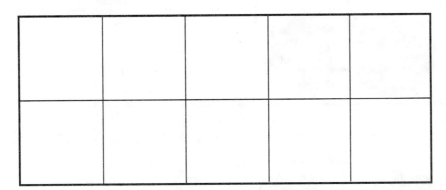

8
eight

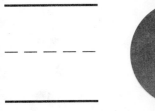

_____  **and** _____

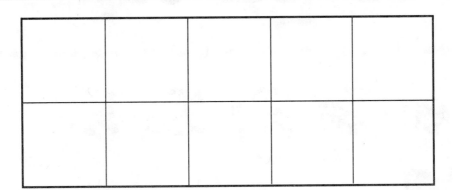

8
eight

_____  **and** _____

DIRECTIONS 1. Draw some red and yellow counters to make 8. Write to show the number of red and yellow counters. 2. Draw some red and yellow counters to make 8 another way. Write to show the number of red and yellow counters.

Lesson Check

3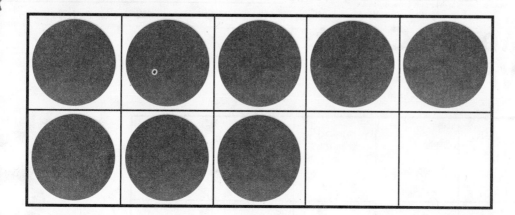

○ **8**

○ **7**

4

○ **6**

○ **8**

5

○ **8**

○ **9**

DIRECTIONS Choose the correct answer.
3. What number does the model show? **4.** How many puppies are there? **5.** How many kittens are there?

126 one hundred twenty-six

© Houghton Mifflin Harcourt Publishing Company

Name _____

4.6 PROBLEM SOLVING • Understand Numbers Through 8

 Essential Question How can you solve problems using the strategy draw a picture?

Unlock the Problem Real World

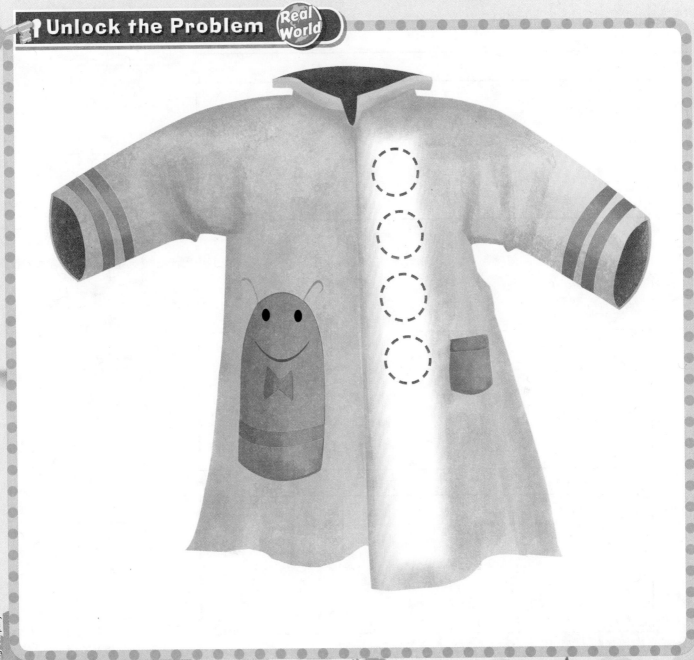

DIRECTIONS There are four buttons on the yellow raincoat. Trace the buttons. Draw more buttons for a total of six. Tell a friend about your drawing.

1

2

DIRECTIONS **1.** George has 5 marbles. Alex has a number of marbles that is two greater than 5. Draw the marbles. Write the numbers. **2.** Allison has 8 crayons. Jackie has the same number of crayons as Allison. Draw the crayons. Write the numbers.

128 one hundred twenty-eight

© Houghton Mifflin Harcourt Publishing Company

Name _____

DIRECTIONS **3.** Ben has 7 rocks. Molly has a number of rocks that is two less than 7. Draw the rocks. Write the numbers. **4.** Jasmine has 4 stickers. Sadie has a number of stickers that is two more than 4. Draw the stickers. Write the numbers.

HOME ACTIVITY • Give your child 8 small items such as buttons. Have your child count the items and tell you how many.

5

6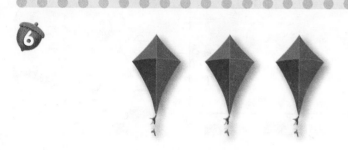

7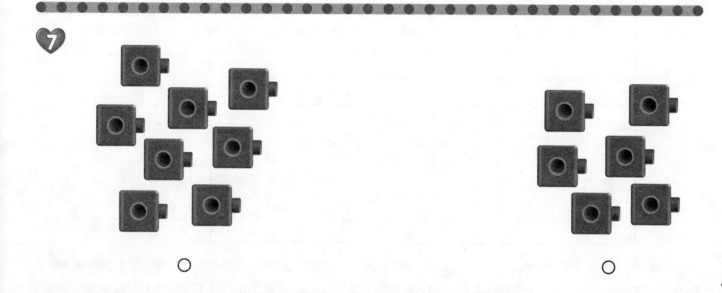

○   ○

DIRECTIONS **5.** Draw a set of blue kites that has two more than the red kites. **6.** Draw a set of red kites that has the same number as the blue kites. **7.** Choose the correct answer. Which group has one more than 7?

130 one hundred thirty

4.6 Understand Numbers Through 8

1

2

DIRECTIONS **1.** Jeremy has 6 balloons. Chad has a number of balloons that is one more than 6. Draw the balloons. Write the numbers. **2.** Diane has 8 pencils. Jill has a number of pencils that is two less than 8. Draw the pencils. Write the numbers.

© Houghton Mifflin Harcourt Publishing Company

○ **8**

○ **7**

○ **6**

○ **2**

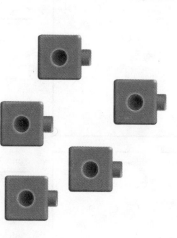

○   ○

DIRECTIONS Choose the correct answer.
3. There is a number of banners that is two more than 6. How many banners are there? **4.** Joe has a number of hats that is two less than 8. How many hats does he have? **5.** Which group has two more than 5?

Name _____

  **Module 4 Assessment**

_____

_ _ _ _ _ _ _ _ _

_____

_ _ _ _ _ _ _ _ _

_____

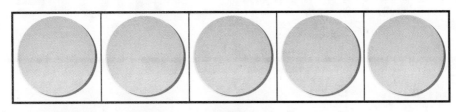

_____

_ _ _ _ _ _ _ _ _

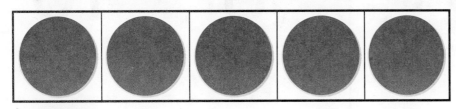

_____

_ _ _ _ _ _ _ _ _

_____

DIRECTIONS 1. Write the number of objects in each set. ◆TEKS K.2.B **2–3.** Count and tell how many. Write the number. ◆TEKS K.2.B

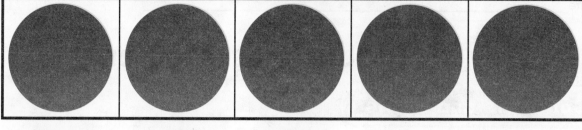

_____
_ _ _ _ _
_____

5 and $\underline{}$ more

8   10
  ○   ○

DIRECTIONS 4. Place counters as shown. Count and tell how many. Write the number. 🔹 TEKS K.2.B **5.** How many more than 5 is 8? Write the number. 🔹 TEKS K.2.B
6. Mark under the number that shows how many eggs. 🔹 TEKS K.2.B

TEKS **Number and Operations—K.2.B**
Also K.2.I
MATHEMATICAL PROCESSES
K.1.E

5.1

HANDS ON

Model and Count 9

? Essential Question

How can you show and count 9 objects?

Explore

DIRECTIONS Model 8 objects. Show one more object. How many are there? Tell a friend how you know. Draw the objects.

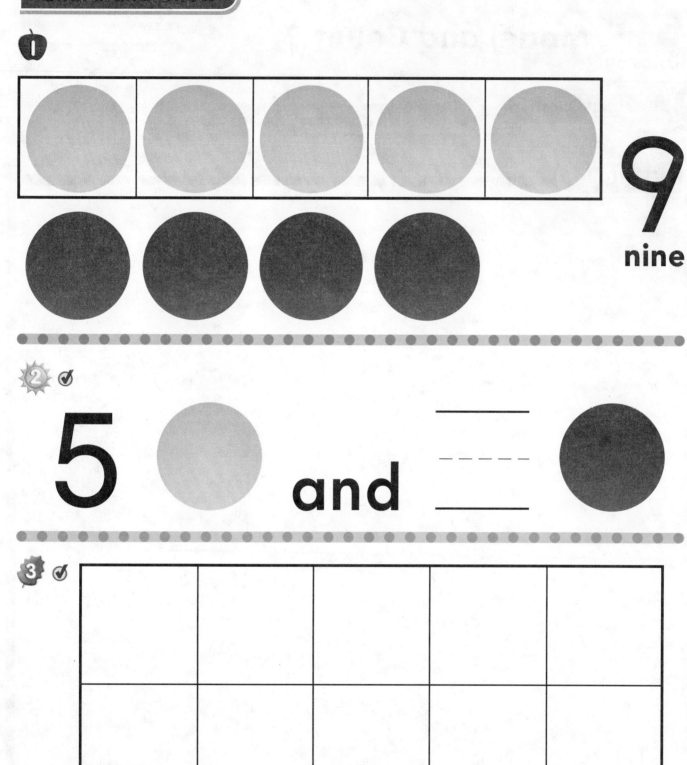

1

9 nine

2 ✓

5 [circle] and ____ [circle]

3 ✓

DIRECTIONS **I.** Place counters as shown. Count and tell how many counters. **2.** 5 are yellow. How many are red? Write the number. **3.** Place counters in the ten frame to model nine. Trace the counters. Tell a friend what you know about the number 9.

Name _____

9
nine

___ ___ ___ ___ 〇

and

___ ___ ___ ___ 〇

and

___ ___ ___ ___ 〇

and

___ ___ ___ ___ 〇

and

● ___ ___ ___ ___

● ___ ___ ___ ___

● ___ ___ ___ ___

● ___ ___ ___ ___

© Houghton Mifflin Harcourt Publishing Company

DIRECTIONS 4. Use two-color counters to model the different ways to make 9. Write to show some pairs of numbers that make 9.

HOME ACTIVITY • Ask your child to show a set of eight objects. Have him or her show one more object and tell how many.

 **Mathematical Processes**
Model • Reason • Communicate

Problem Solving Real World

5

Daily Assessment Task

6

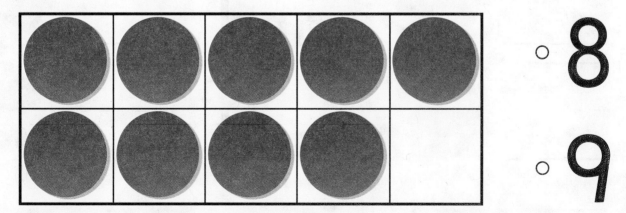

○ **8**

○ **9**

DIRECTIONS 5. Count the flags in each set. Which sets show nine flags? Circle those sets. **6.** Choose the correct answer. Which number does the model show?

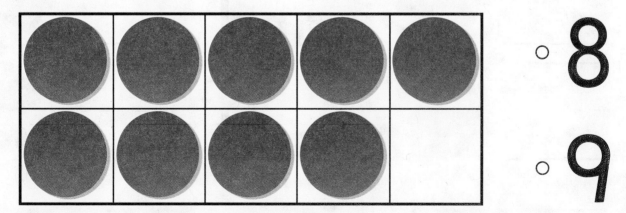

138 one hundred thirty-eight

TEKS **Number and Operations—K.2.B**
Also K.2.I
MATHEMATICAL PROCESSES K.1.E

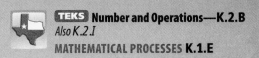

Name _____

5.1
HANDS ON

Model and Count 9

 ❶

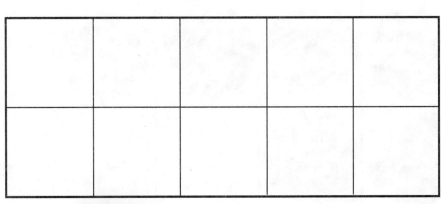

9
nine

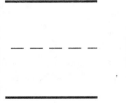  _ _ _ _ _ _ **and** _ _ _ _ _ _

❷

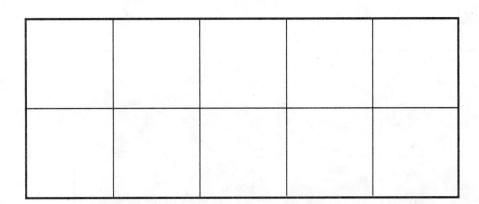

9
nine

 _ _ _ _ _ _ **and** _ _ _ _ _ _

DIRECTIONS **1.** Draw some red and yellow counters to make 9. Write to show the numbers. **2.** Draw some red and yellow counters to show another way to make 9. Write to show the numbers.

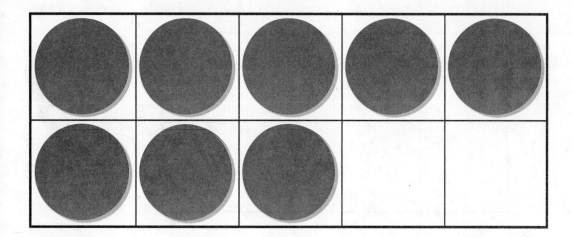

○ 9

○ 8

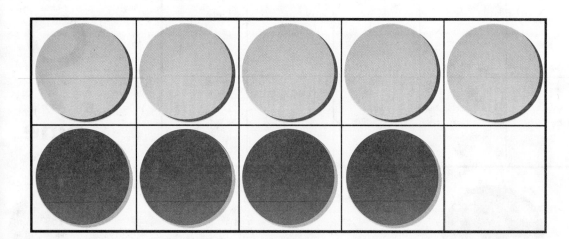

○ 9

○ 8

DIRECTIONS Choose the correct answer.
3–4. Which number does the model show?

5.2 Count and Write 9

TEKS Number and Operations—K.2.B

MATHEMATICAL PROCESSES
K.1.A

? Essential Question How can you count and write 9 with words and numbers?

Explore Real World

DIRECTIONS Count and tell how many cubes. Write the numbers. Count and tell how many ducks. Trace the word.

1

DIRECTIONS 1. Look at the picture. Circle the sets of nine objects.

9

nine

---

3 ✓

_____

- - - - -

_____

4

_____

- - - - -

_____

5

_____

- - - - -

_____

6

_____

- - - - -

_____

DIRECTIONS **2.** Say the number. Write the numbers. **3–6.** Count and tell how many. Write the number.

HOME ACTIVITY • Ask your child to find something in your home that has the number 9 on it, such as a clock or a phone.

Module 5 • Lesson 2

one hundred forty-three **143**

Problem Solving Real World

7

Daily Assessment Task

8

○   ○

DIRECTIONS **7.** Which set has a number of objects one less than 10?
Circle that set. **8.** Choose the correct answer. Which set has nine ducks?

TEKS **Number and Operations—K.2.B**
MATHEMATICAL PROCESSES **K.1.A**

Name _____

5.2 Count and Write 9

1

_____

- - - - - - -

_____

2

_____

- - - - - - -

_____

3

_____

- - - - - - -

_____

4

_____

- - - - - - -

_____

DIRECTIONS 1–4. Count and tell how many. Write the number.

5

○   ○

6

○   ○

DIRECTIONS Choose the correct answer.
5. Which set has 9 hats? 6. Which set has
9 footballs?

Name _____

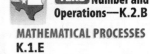
5.3 Model, Count, and Write 10

Essential Question

How can you show, count, and write 10?

Explore

Hands On

DIRECTIONS Use counters to show 9 in the top ten frame.
Use counters to show 10 in the bottom ten frame. Draw the counters.

10
ten

_____

- - - - - - - -

_____

_____

- - - - - - - -

_____

_____

- - - - - - - -

_____

_____

- - - - - - - -

_____

DIRECTIONS **1.** Count and tell how many eggs. Trace the number. **2–5.** Count and tell how many eggs. Write the number.

Name _____

© Houghton Mifflin Harcourt Publishing Company

 6

10
ten

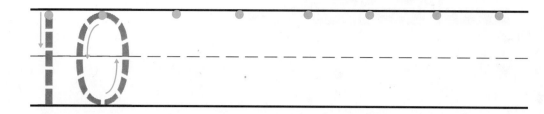

 7

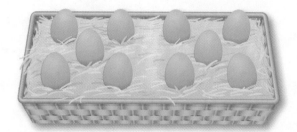

 8

 9

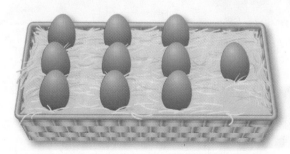

DIRECTIONS **6.** Say the number. Trace and write the numbers. **7–9.** Count and tell how many. Write the number.

HOME ACTIVITY • Ask your child to show a set of nine objects. Then have him or her show one more object and tell how many objects are in the set.

Problem Solving

10

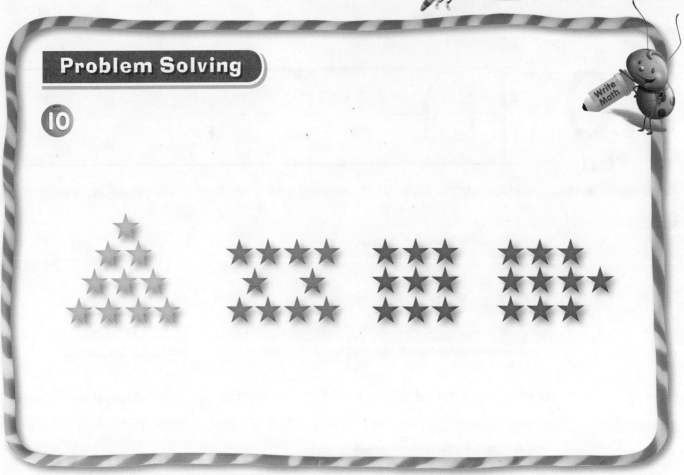

Daily Assessment Task

 11

○

○

DIRECTIONS **10.** Count the stars in each set. Which sets show ten stars? Circle those sets. **11.** Choose the correct answer. Ed counts 10 cubes. Which set is his?

150 one hundred fifty

TEKS Number and Operations—K.2.B
MATHEMATICAL PROCESSES K.1.E

5.3 Model, Count, and Write 10

1

_____

_ _ _ _ _ _ _ _

2

_____

_ _ _ _ _ _ _ _

3

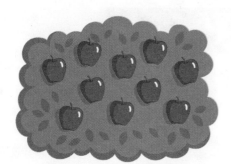

_____

_ _ _ _ _ _ _ _

4

_____

_ _ _ _ _ _ _ _

© Houghton Mifflin Harcourt Publishing Company

Module 5

DIRECTIONS 1–4. Count and tell how many apples. Write the number.

one hundred fifty-one **151**

5

○

○

6

○

○

DIRECTIONS Choose the correct answer.
5. Lesli counts 8 cubes. Which set is hers?
6. Lennie counts 10 cubes. Which set is his?

Name _____

5.4 PROBLEM SOLVING • Ways to Make 10

TEKS **Number and Operations—K.2.B**
Also K.2.I
MATHEMATICAL PROCESSES
K.1.A, K.1.B

? Essential Question

How can you solve a problem using the strategy draw a picture?

🔑 Unlock the Problem

DIRECTIONS Use cubes of two colors to show different ways to make 10. Color to show the ways.

Module 5

one hundred fifty-three **153**

© Houghton Mifflin Harcourt Publishing Company

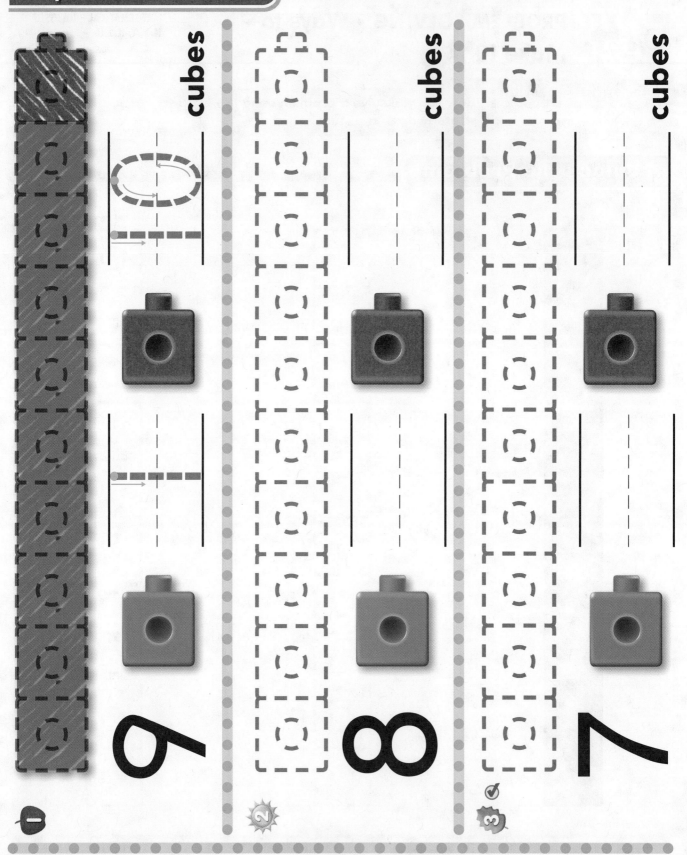

cubes

cubes

cubes

9

8

7

DIRECTIONS **I.** Count and tell how many cubes of each color there are. Trace the numbers. **2–3.** Color cubes blue to match the number. Color the other cubes red to make 10. Write how many cubes. Write how many cubes in all.

cubes

_____ cubes

_____ cubes

5

3

2

❀ 4

✿ 5

🌰 6

© Houghton Mifflin Harcourt Publishing Company

DIRECTIONS   4–6. Color cubes blue to match the number. Color the other cubes red to make 10. Write how many red cubes. Write how many cubes in all.

HOME ACTIVITY • Ask your child to show a set of 10 objects. Have him or her write numbers to show the set.

7

○ 10

○ 5

8

○ 3   ○ 2

9

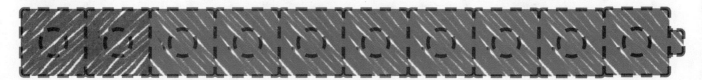

○ 2  and 8   ○ 1  and 9

DIRECTIONS Choose the correct answer. **7.** Ella has ten toy trucks. Which number shows how many trucks she has? **8.** How many more cubes should you color to make 10? **9.** How is 10 shown in the cube train?

156 one hundred fifty-six

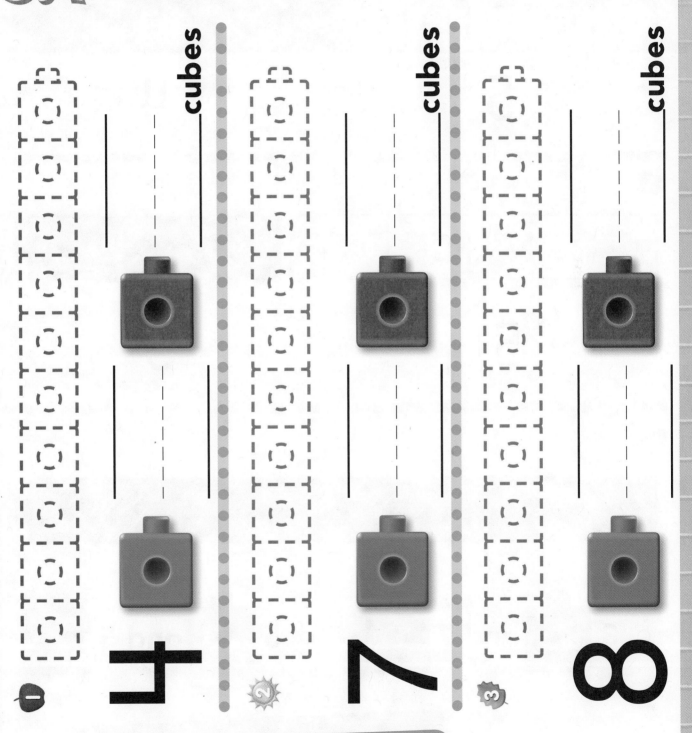
Name _____

5.4 PROBLEM SOLVING • Ways to Make 10

cubes

cubes

cubes

❶ 4

② 7

③ 8

DIRECTIONS 1–3. Use blue to color the cubes to match the number. Use red to color the other cubes. Write how many red cubes. Write how many cubes in all.

Lesson Check

4

○ **5**　　　　　　○ **4**

5

○ **5**　　　　　　○ **6**

6

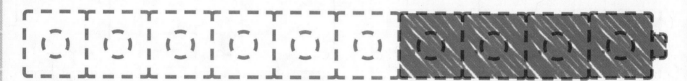

○ **3**  **and 7** 　　○ **5** **and 5**

DIRECTIONS Choose the correct answer.
4–5. How many more cubes should you color to make 10? **6.** How is 10 shown on the cube train?

158 one hundred fifty-eight

Module 5 Assessment

Concepts and Skills

 1

_____   _____

_ _ _ _ _ _ _ _      _ _ _ _ _ _ _ _

_____   _____

 2

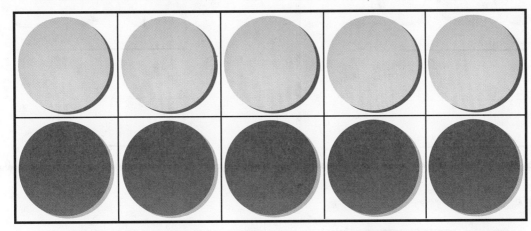

_____   _____

 _ _ _ _ _ _ _ _   _ _ _ _ _ _ _ _

_____   _____

DIRECTIONS **1–2.** Count and tell how many yellow counters. Write the number. Count and tell how many red counters. Write the number. ⬇ TEKS K.2.B

3

_____

- - - - - - - - -

_____

4

_____

- - - - - - - - -

_____

5

_____

- - - - - - - - -

_____

6

_____

- - - - - - - - -

_____

7 ⭐ **TEXAS Test Prep**

○ **7** ◻ **3** ◻   ○ **9** ◻ **1** ◻

DIRECTIONS   3–6. Count the objects. Write the number. 🔷 TEKS K.2.B
7. Choose the correct answer. Which shows how many blue and red cubes? 🔷 TEKS K.2.I

160 one hundred sixty

TEKS **Number and Operations—K.2.B, K.2.C**
MATHEMATICAL PROCESSES
K.1.A, K.1.F

6.1 Count and Order to 10

? Essential Question How do you count forward to 10 from a given number?

Explore

1 2 3 4 5 6 7 8 9 10

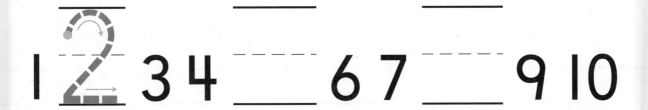

1 2 3 4 ___ ___ 6 7 ___ ___ 9 10

DIRECTIONS Point to the numbers in the top workspace as you count forward to 10. Trace and write the numbers in order in the bottom workspace as you count forward to 10.

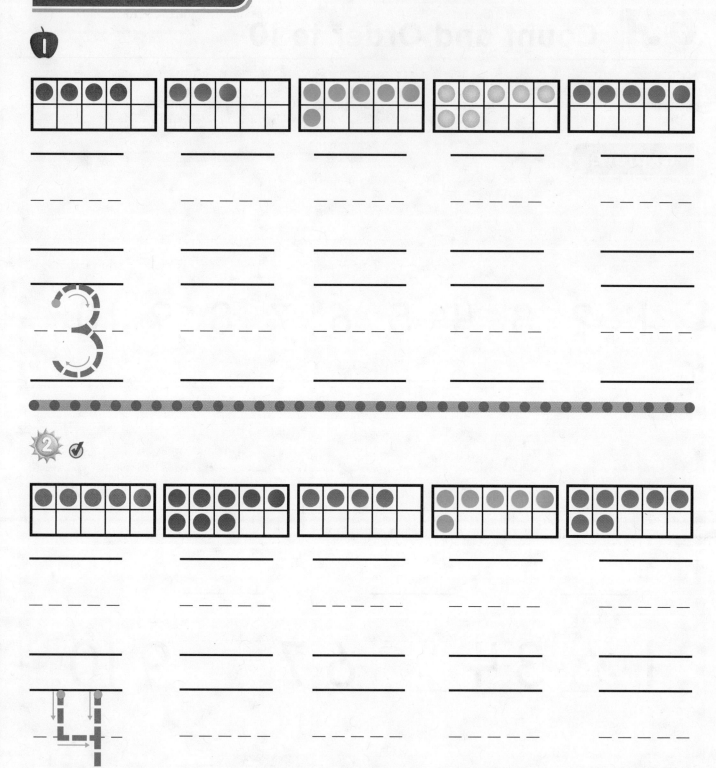

DIRECTIONS **1–2.** Count the dots of each color in the ten frames. Write the numbers. Look at the next line. Write the numbers in order as you count forward starting from the dashed number.

Name _____

❸

_____   _____   _____   _____   _____

- - - - -   - - - - -   - - - - -   - - - - -   - - - - -

_____   _____   _____   _____   _____

_____   _____   _____   _____   _____

5

● ●

❹

_____   _____   _____   _____   _____

- - - - -   - - - - -   - - - - -   - - - - -   - - - - -

_____   _____   _____   _____   _____

_____   _____   _____   _____   _____

6

● ●

DIRECTIONS 3–4. Count the dots of each color in the ten frames. Write the numbers. On the next line, write the numbers in order as you count forward starting from the dashed number.

HOME ACTIVITY • Write the numbers 1 to 10 in order on a piece of paper. Ask your child to point to each number as he or she counts to 10. Repeat beginning with a number other than 1 when counting.

Problem Solving Real World

5

5   6   ____
         - - - -
         ____

8   ____   10
     - - - -
     ____

Daily Assessment Task

6

9   10
○   ○

DIRECTIONS **5.** Kate listed the numbers 5 through 10 in order. Look at the numbers. Write the numbers that are missing from Kate's list. **6.** Choose the correct answer. How many footprints are there?

TEKS **Number and Operations—K.2.B, K.2.C**
MATHEMATICAL PROCESSES **K.1.A**

6.1 Count and Order to 10

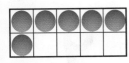 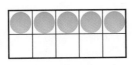 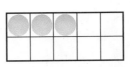  

_____ _____ _____ _____ _____

- -

_____ _____ _____ _____ _____

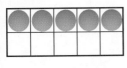 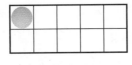 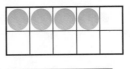 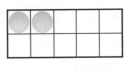 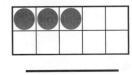

_____ _____ _____ _____ _____

- -

_____ _____ _____ _____ _____

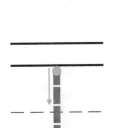

DIRECTIONS 1–2. Count the dots of each color in the ten frames. Write the numbers. On the next line, write the numbers in order as you count forward starting from the dashed number.

3

○ **8**

○ **9**

4

○ **9**

○ **10**

5

○ **6**

○ **7**

DIRECTIONS Choose the correct answer.
3. How many balloons are there? **4.** How many butterflies are there? **5.** How many flowers are there?

166 one hundred sixty-six

© Houghton Mifflin Harcourt Publishing Company

HANDS ON

Compare by Matching Sets to 10

TEKS **Number and Operations—K.2.G**
Also K.2.B
MATHEMATICAL PROCESSES
K.1.E

? Essential Question

How can you use matching to compare sets to 10?

Explore

DIRECTIONS Make a cube train with 3 cubes. Make a cube train with 6 cubes. Compare the cube trains. Draw the cubes. Circle the set that has fewer cubes.

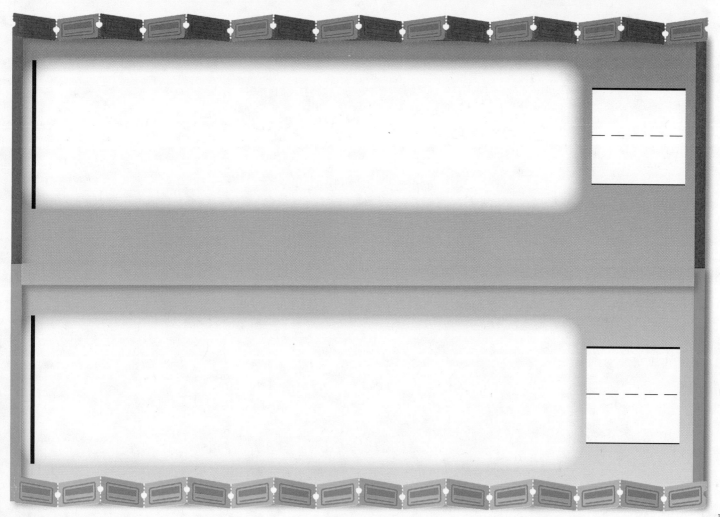

DIRECTIONS **I.** Make red and blue cube trains to model the numbers of balloons in the sets. Compare the cube trains by matching. Draw and color the cube trains. Write how many in each set. Circle the cube train that has more cubes.

Name _____

DIRECTIONS **2.** Make a 5-cube train and a 7-cube train. Compare the cube trains by matching. Draw and color the cube trains. Write how many. Circle the cube train with fewer cubes. **3.** Make a 6-cube train and a 4-cube train. Compare the cube trains by matching. Draw and color the cube trains. Write how many. Circle the cube train with fewer cubes.

HOME ACTIVITY • Ask your child to show two sets of up to 10 objects each. Then have him or her compare the sets by matching and tell which set has more objects.

Module 6 • Lesson 2

one hundred sixty-nine **169**

Problem Solving

4

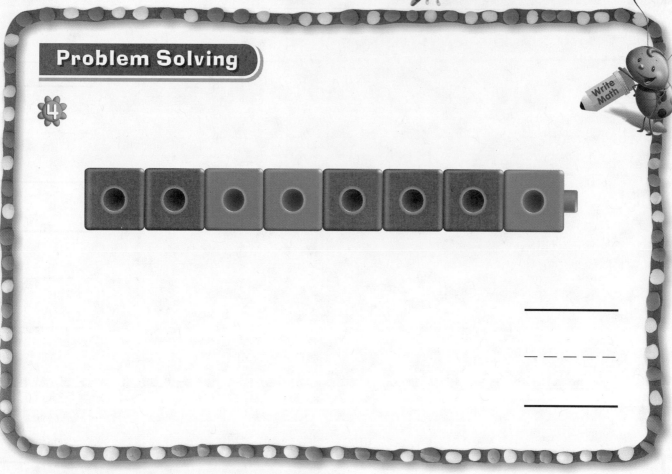

Daily Assessment Task

5

DIRECTIONS **4.** Look at the cube train. Are there more blue cubes or more red cubes? Make cube trains of each color. Compare the cube trains by matching. Draw and color the cube train that has more cubes. Write the number. **5.** Choose the correct answer. Which cube train has more cubes?

170 one hundred seventy

© Houghton Mifflin Harcourt Publishing Company

Homework and Practice

Name _____

6.2
HANDS ON

Compare by Matching Sets to 10

1

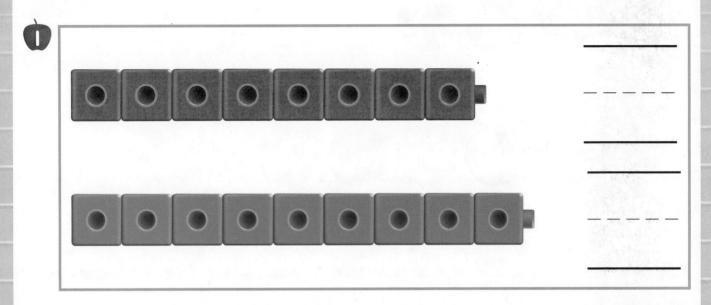

2

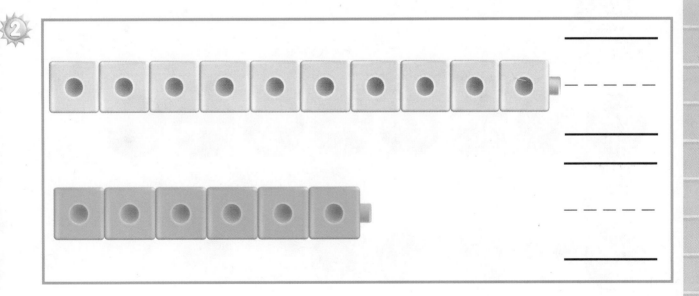

DIRECTIONS **1–2.** Compare the cube trains by matching. Write how many. Circle the cube train with fewer cubes.

3

○

○

4

○

○

DIRECTIONS Choose the correct answer.
3–4. Are there more red counters or yellow counters?

TEKS **Number and Operations—K.2.G**

MATHEMATICAL PROCESSES
K.1.E

6.3 Compare by Counting Sets to 10

How can you use counting to compare sets of objects to 10?

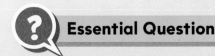 **Explore** Real World

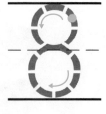

DIRECTIONS Look at the sets of objects. Count how many in each set. Use cubes to keep track of the objects that have been counted. Trace the numbers that show how many. Compare the numbers. Circle the greater number.

1

_____

- - - - - - - - -

_____

_____

- - - - - - - - -

_____

2 ✓

_____

- - - - - - - - -

_____

_____

- - - - - - - - -

_____

3 ✓

_____

- - - - - - - - -

_____

_____

- - - - - - - - -

_____

DIRECTIONS **1–3.** Count how many in each set. Write the number of objects in each set. Compare the numbers. Circle the greater number.

Name _____

4

_____

‒ ‒ ‒ ‒ ‒ ‒ ‒ ‒

_____

_____

‒ ‒ ‒ ‒ ‒ ‒ ‒ ‒

_____

5

_____

‒ ‒ ‒ ‒ ‒ ‒ ‒ ‒

_____

_____

‒ ‒ ‒ ‒ ‒ ‒ ‒ ‒

_____

6

_____

‒ ‒ ‒ ‒ ‒ ‒ ‒ ‒

_____

_____

‒ ‒ ‒ ‒ ‒ ‒ ‒ ‒

_____

DIRECTIONS 4–6. Count how many in each set. Write the number of objects in each set. Compare the numbers. Circle the number that is less.

HOME ACTIVITY • Show your child two sets of up to 10 objects. Have your child write the number of objects in each set. Ask which number is greater.

Problem Solving *Real World*

7

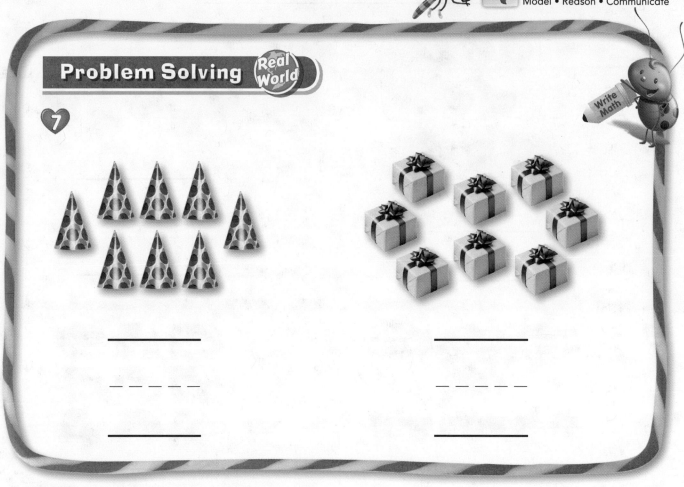

_____

- - - - - - -

_____

            _____

            - - - - - - -

            _____

Daily Assessment Task

8

      ○   ○

DIRECTIONS 7. Megan bought hats and gifts for the party. Count how many in each set. Write the number of objects in each set. Compare the numbers. Tell a friend about the sets. **8.** Choose the correct answer. Compare the sets. Which set has more backpacks?

TEKS Number and Operations—K.2.G
MATHEMATICAL PROCESSES K.1.E

Name _____

6.3 Compare by Counting Sets to 10

_____

- - - - - - - -

_____

_____

- - - - - - - -

_____

_____

- - - - - - - -

_____

_____

- - - - - - - -

_____

DIRECTIONS 1–2. Count how many in each set. Write the number of objects in each set. Compare the numbers. Circle the greater number.

3

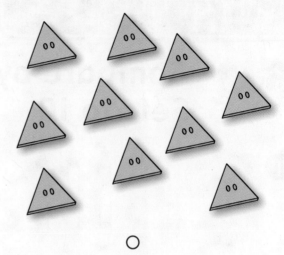

○   ○

4

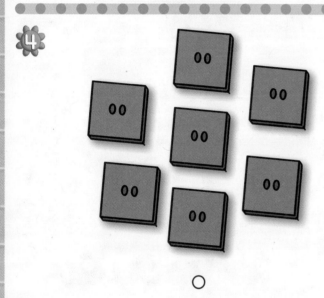

○   ○

5

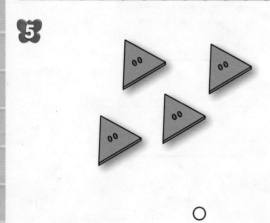

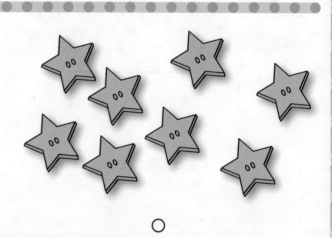

○   ○

DIRECTIONS Choose the correct answer.
3–5. Compare the sets. Which set has fewer?

6.4 One More and One Less

TEKS Number and Operations— K.2.E, K.2.F
MATHEMATICAL PROCESSES K.1.E

? Essential Question

How can you find a number that is one more than or one less than another number?

Explore

_____   8   _____

DIRECTIONS Place 8 counters in the ten frame. Take one counter away. Write the number that is one less than 8. Place 8 counters in the ten frame again. Add one more counter. Write the number that is one more than 8.

Share and Show

_____ 6 _ _ _ _ _

_ _ _ _ _ 3 _ _ _ _ _

DIRECTIONS **1.** There are 6 erasers in the set. Write the number that is one less than 6. Write the number that is one more than 6. **2.** There are 3 crayons in the set. Write the number that is one less than 3. Write the number that is one more than 3.

180 one hundred eighty

Name _____

 3

_____   9   _____

- - - - - -   - - - - - -

_____   _____

4

_____   2   _____

- - - - - -   - - - - - -

_____   _____

5

_____   4   _____

- - - - - -   - - - - - -

_____   _____

DIRECTIONS   3–5. Look at the number. Write the number that is one less. Write the number that is one more.

HOME ACTIVITY • Show your child a set of seven household objects. Have your child create a set of objects that has one more object than your set.

Module 6 • Lesson 4   one hundred eighty-one **181**

Problem Solving Real World

6

_____

- - - - - - -

_____

Daily Assessment Task

_____

- - - - - - -

_____

DIRECTIONS **6.** Gabe has 5 hats. Chloe has one more hat than Gabe. How many hats does Chloe have? Draw Chloe's hats. Write the number. **7.** Jack has 3 marbles. Pat has one more marble than Jack. Draw Pat's marbles and write how many.

182 one hundred eighty-two

6.4 One More and One Less

1

_____   **7**   _ _ _ _ _ _ _
_____   _____

2

_ _ _ _ _ _ _   **8**   _ _ _ _ _ _ _
_____   _____

3

_ _ _ _ _ _ _   **5**   _ _ _ _ _ _ _
_____   _____

DIRECTIONS 1. There are 7 pencils in the set.
Write the number that is one less than 7. Write
the number that is one more than 7. **2–3.** Look
at the number. Write the number that is one less.
Write the number that is one more.

　　　　○　　　　　　　　　　　　○

　　　　○　　　　　　　　　　　　○

DIRECTIONS Choose the correct answer.
4. Jessica has a sticker with 4 stars. Which sticker
has 1 more star? **5.** Beth has a picture of
10 flowers. Which picture has a number of flowers
that is 1 less than 10?

TEKS Number and
Operations—K.2.E

MATHEMATICAL PROCESSES
K.1.E

6.5 Make a Set
HANDS ON

? **Essential Question**

How can you make a set to show a number that is more than, less than, or the same as a number?

Explore

DIRECTIONS Make a set of 6 counters in the top workspace. Draw the counters. Trace the number. In the bottom workspace, make a set of counters that has two fewer than 6. Draw the counters. Write the number.

_____

- - - - - - -

_____

●●

_____

- - - - - - -

_____

●●

DIRECTIONS 1. Use counters to make a set that is two more than 3. Draw the counters. Write the number. **2.** Use counters to make a set that is the same as 3. Draw the counters. Write the number.

Name _____

_____

– – – – – – – –

_____

● ●

4

_____

– – – – – – – –

_____

● ●

DIRECTIONS **3.** Use counters to make a set that is less than 7. Draw the counters. Write the number. **4.** Use counters to make a set that is more than 4. Draw the counters. Write the number.

HOME ACTIVITY • Choose a number between 1 and 10. Using household items, have your child create a set that is more than or less than that number.

Module 6 • Lesson 5

Problem Solving Real World

5

_____

- - - - - -

_____

Daily Assessment Task

6

◯   ◯

DIRECTIONS 5. Morgan found two leaves. Joe found two more leaves than Morgan. How many leaves did Joe find? Draw Joe's leaves. Write the number. **6.** Choose the correct answer. Caleb has 6 beach balls. Which set has more beach balls than Caleb has?

Name _____

6.5 **Make a Set**

HANDS ON

1

2

DIRECTIONS I. Draw some counters to make a set that is less than 10. Write the number. **2.** Draw some counters to make a set that is more than 6. Write the number.

○   ○

○   ○

DIRECTIONS Choose the correct answer.
3. Jose has 7 toy cars. Which set has more toy cars than Jose? **4.** Marta has 4 leaves. Which set has a number of leaves that is less than 4?

190 one hundred ninety

Name _____

6.6
HANDS ON

PROBLEM SOLVING • Compare Numbers to 10

Essential Question
How can you solve problems using the strategy make a model?

Unlock the Problem

DIRECTIONS Carlos has 7 cubes. Jenny has one more cube than Carlos. How many cubes does Jenny have? Show the cubes. Compare the sets of cubes. Draw the cubes. Circle the set of cubes that has more.

Try Another Problem

1 ✓

_____

- - - - - - - - -

_____

_____

- - - - - - - - -

_____

DIRECTIONS **1.** Paul has 3 blocks. Brody has two more blocks than Paul. Use cubes to model the sets of blocks. Compare the sets. Which set has more? Draw the cubes. Write how many in each set. Circle the greater number. Tell a friend how you compared the numbers.

192 one hundred ninety-two

Share and Show

_____

- - - - - - - - -

_____

_____

- - - - - - - - -

_____

DIRECTIONS   2. Libby has 7 beads. Madeline has three fewer beads than Libby. Use cubes to model the sets of beads. Compare the sets. Which set has fewer cubes? Draw the cubes. Write how many in each set. Circle the number that is less. Tell a friend how you compared the numbers.

HOME ACTIVITY • Have your child count two sets of objects in your home, and write how many are in each set. Then have him or her circle the greater number. Repeat with sets of different numbers.

Daily Assessment Task

○ 6 is less than 7

○ 6 is greater than 7

○ 4 is less than 3

○ 4 is greater than 3

10

8

○   ○

DIRECTIONS Choose the correct answer. **3.** There are 6 ladybugs. Which is true about the number 6? **4.** There are 4 dogs. Which is true about the number 4? **5.** Choose the correct answer. Which number is greater?

194 one hundred ninety-four

TEKS Number and Operations—K.2.G, K.2.H
MATHEMATICAL PROCESSES K.1.B

6.6 HANDS ON
PROBLEM SOLVING • Compare Numbers to 10

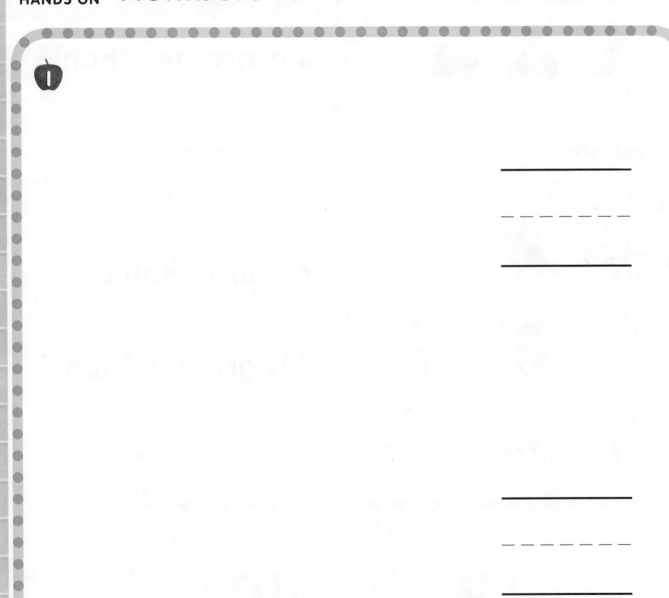

1

_____

- - - - - - - - - - - -

_____

_____

- - - - - - - - - - - -

_____

DIRECTIONS I. Tony has 4 marbles. Joey has three more marbles than Tony. Draw to model the sets of marbles. Compare the sets. Which set has more marbles? Write how many in each set. Circle the greater number. Tell how you compared the numbers.

2

○ **5 is less than 6**

○ **5 is greater than 6**

3

○ **7 is less than 6**

○ **7 is greater than 6**

4

4

10

○   ○

DIRECTIONS Choose the correct answer.
2. There are five bears. What is true about 5?
3. There are 7 bunnies. What is true about 7?
4. Which number is greater?

Name _____

 Module 6 Assessment

3

© Houghton Mifflin Harcourt Publishing Company

DIRECTIONS I. Count the dots of each color in the ten frames. Write the numbers. Trace and write the numbers in order as you count forward from the dashed number. ⬦ TEKS K.2.C **2.** Make a cube train with 6 cubes. Make a cube train with 4 cubes. Compare the cube trains by matching. Draw the cube trains. Write how many. Circle the cube train with more cubes. ⬦ TEKS K.2.G

_____

- - - - - - - -

_____

_____   _____

- - - - - - - -   - - - - - -

 4   _____   **5**   _____

- - - - - - - -   - - - - - -

_____   _____

 5    6

❤ 7   ⭐ **TEXAS Test Prep**   🐟 8

5   3   7   9

○   ○   ○   ○

DIRECTIONS 3. Write the number of objects in each set. Circle the greater number. 🔶 TEKS K.2.G **4.** Look at the number. Write the number that is one less. Write the number that is one more. 🔶 TEKS K.2.F **5.** Draw a set that has one fewer apple. **6.** Look at the marbles. Draw a set that has fewer. 🔶 TEKS K.2.E **7–8.** Choose the correct answer. Which number is greater? 🔶 TEKS K.2.F

TEKS Number and Operations—K.2.B
Also K.2.A, K.2.C
MATHEMATICAL PROCESSES
K.1.E, K.1.D, K.1.G

7.1 HANDS ON
Model and Count 11 and 12

? **Essential Question**

How do you use objects to show 11 and 12 as ten and some more?

Explore

DIRECTIONS Use counters to show the number 11. Add more to show the number 12. Draw the counters.

1

11
eleven

12
twelve

2 ✓

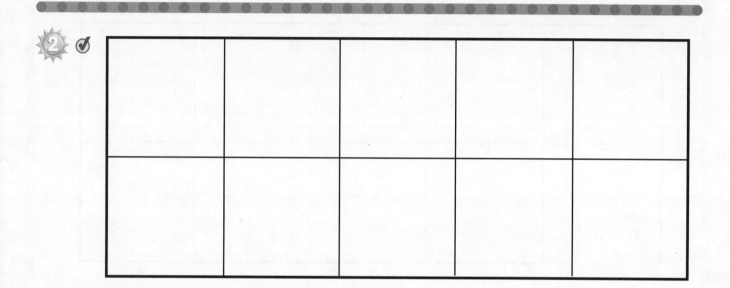

3 _____   _____

_ _ _ _ _ _ _ _   _ _ _ _ _ _ _

_____ **and** _____

DIRECTIONS **1.** Count and tell how many. Circle the number and word.
2. Use counters to show the number 11. Draw the counters. **3.** Look at the counters you drew. How many are in the ten frame? Write the number. How many more are there? Write the number.

4 # 12
twelve

11
eleven

 5

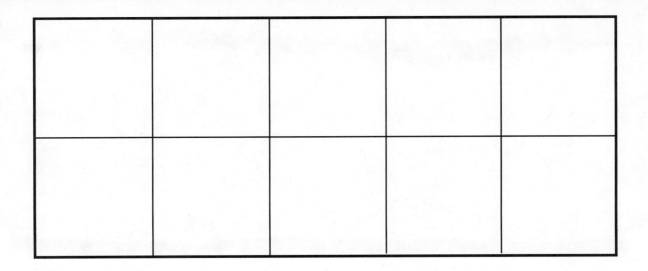

6 _____   _____

- - - - - - - -   - - - - - - - -

and

_____   _____

DIRECTIONS 4. Count and tell how many. Circle the number and word.   **5.** Use counters to show the number 12. Draw the counters.   **6.** Look at the counters you drew. How many are in the ten frame? Write the number. How many more are there? Write the number.

 HOME ACTIVITY • Draw a ten frame on a sheet of paper. Have your child use small objects such as buttons, pennies, or dried beans to show the numbers 11 and 12.

Module 7 • Lesson 1

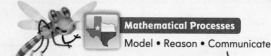

Problem Solving Real World

7

Daily Assessment Task

8

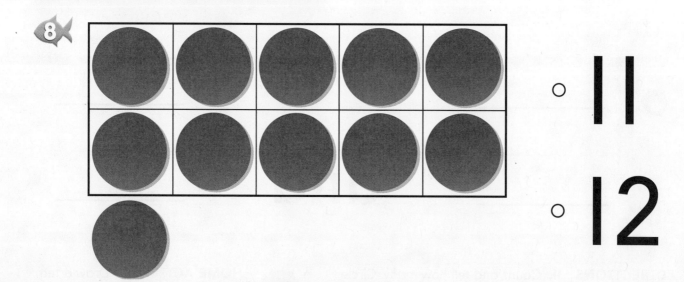

○ 11

○ 12

DIRECTIONS **7.** Start with the blue bead on the left. Circle to show 11 beads on the bead string. **8.** Choose the correct answer. How many counters are there?

202 two hundred two

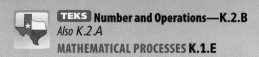
Homework and Practice

Name _____

7.1 HANDS ON
Model and Count 11 and 12

1

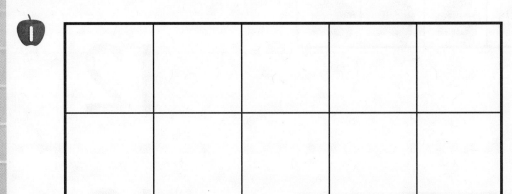

_____

- - - - - - - - - - - -

_____

2

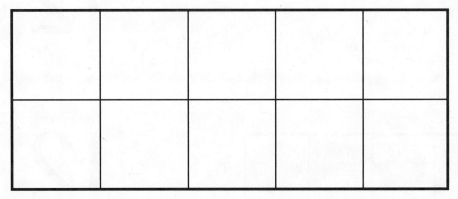

_____

- - - - - - - - - - - -

_____

DIRECTIONS **1.** Draw counters to show 11. Write the number. **2.** Draw counters to show 12. Write the number.

3

○ 11

○ 12

4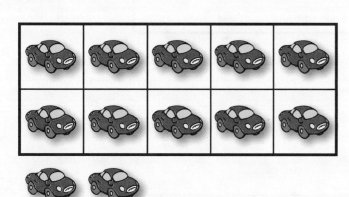

○ 10

○ 12

5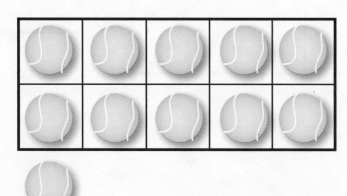

○ 12

○ 11

DIRECTIONS Choose the correct answer.
3. How many bears are there? **4.** How many cars are there? **5.** How many balls are there?

7.2 Count and Write 11 and 12

TEKS Number and Operations—K.2.B
Also K.2.A, K.2.C
MATHEMATICAL PROCESSES
K.1.D

? Essential Question

How do you count and write 11 and 12 with words and numbers?

Explore

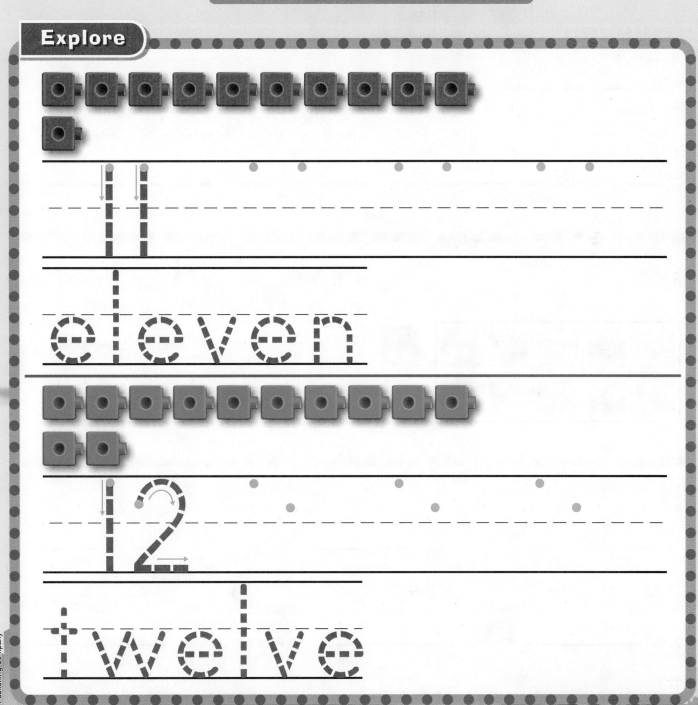

DIRECTIONS Count and tell how many. Trace and write the numbers and the words.

Share and Show

1

eleven

_____

- -

_____

2 ✓

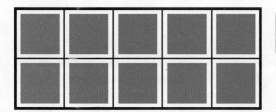

_____

- - - - - - - -

_____

3

_____   _____   _____

- - - -   - - - -   - - - -

_____   _____   _____

DIRECTIONS **1.** Count and tell how many. Practice writing the number. **2.** Count and tell how many. Write the number. **3.** Look at the squares in Exercise 2. Write how many blue squares. Write how many red squares. Write how many squares in all.

206 two hundred six

4

12
twelve

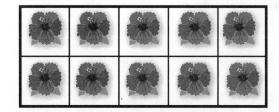

 5

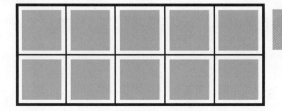

 6

DIRECTIONS **4.** Count and tell how many. Practice writing the number. **5.** Count and tell how many. Write the number. **6.** Look at the squares in Exercise 5. Write how many green squares. Write how many orange squares. Write how many squares in all.

 HOME ACTIVITY • Ask your child to count and write the number for a set of 11 or 12 objects, such as macaroni pieces or buttons.

Module 7 • Lesson 2

Problem Solving *Real World*

7

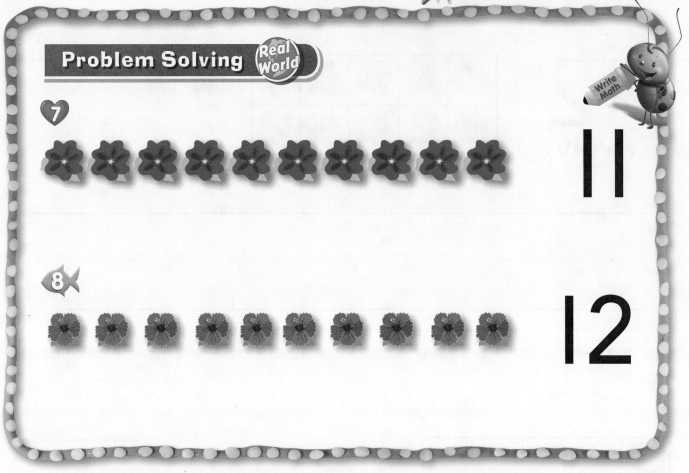

11

8

12

Daily Assessment Task

9

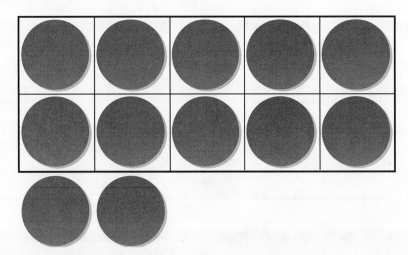

_____

- - - - -

_____

DIRECTIONS **7–8.** Look at the number. Draw more flowers to show that number. **9.** Count the counters. Write the number.

7.2 Count and Write 11 and 12

1 11 eleven

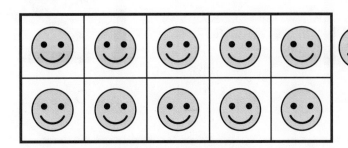

_____

- - - - - - - - - - - - - - -

_____

2 12 twelve

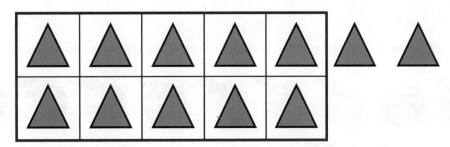

_____

- - - - - - - - - - - - - - -

_____

DIRECTIONS 1–2. Count and tell how many. Practice writing the number.

3.

    | | | 2
     ○   ○

4.

    | | | 2
     ○   ○

5.

    | 0 | |
     ○   ○

DIRECTIONS Choose the correct answer.
3. Count the strawberries. How would you write the number? **4.** Count the pears. How would you write the number? **5.** Count the apples. How would you write the number?

TEKS Number and
Operations—K.2.B
Also K.2.F, K.2.C
MATHEMATICAL PROCESSES
K.1.E, K.1.D, K.1.G

7.3
HANDS ON
Model and Count 13 and 14

? **Essential Question**

How do you use objects to show 13 and 14 as ten and some more?

Explore

DIRECTIONS Use counters to show the number 13. Add more to show the number 14. Draw the counters.

① 13 thirteen   14 fourteen

② ✓

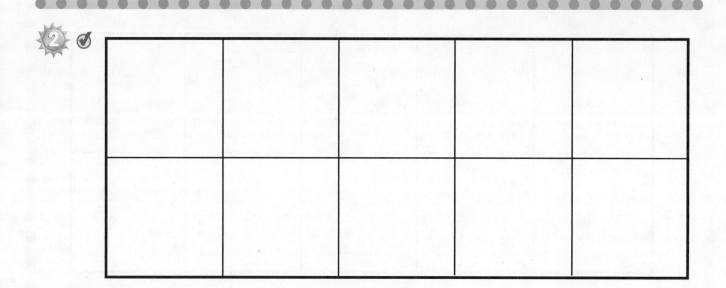

③

_____   _____

_ _ _ _ _   _ _ _ _ _

_____   **and**   _____

DIRECTIONS **1.** Count and tell how many. Circle the number and word. **2.** Use counters to show the number 13. Draw the counters. **3.** Look at the counters you drew. How many are in the ten frame? Write the number. How many more are there? Write the number.

Name _____

14
fourteen

13
thirteen

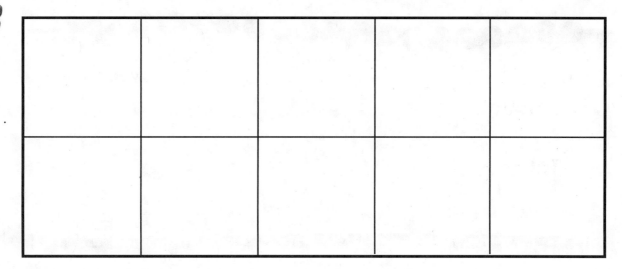

and

_____
- - - - - - -
_____

_____
- - - - - - -
_____

DIRECTIONS **4.** Count and tell how many. Circle the number and word. **5.** Use counters to show the number 14. Draw the counters. **6.** Look at the counters you drew. How many are in the ten frame? Write the number. How many more are there? Write the number.

HOME ACTIVITY • Draw a ten frame on a sheet of paper. Have your child use small objects such as buttons, pennies, or dried beans to show the numbers 13 and 14.

Module 7 • Lesson 3

Mathematical Processes
Model • Reason • Communicate

Problem Solving
Real World

7

Daily Assessment Task

8

○ **13**

○ **14**

DIRECTIONS **7.** Start with the blue bead on the left. Circle to show 13 beads on the bead string. **8.** Choose the correct answer. How many marbles are there?

Name _____

7.3
HANDS ON

Model and Count 13 and 14

1

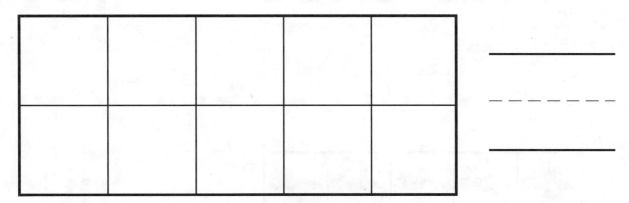

2

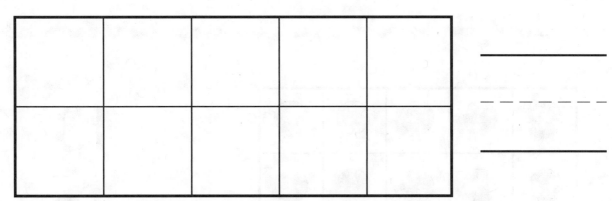

© Houghton Mifflin Harcourt Publishing Company

DIRECTIONS **1.** Draw counters to show 13. Write the number. **2.** Draw counters to show 14. Write the number.

Module 7

two hundred fifteen **215**

3

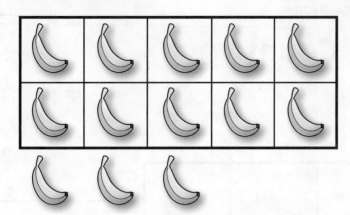

○ **13**

○ **14**

4

○ **14**

○ **13**

5

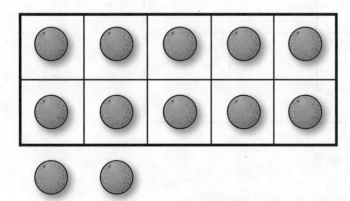

○ **13**

○ **12**

DIRECTIONS Choose the correct answer.
3. How many bananas are there? **4.** How many
pineapples are there? **5.** How many oranges are
there?

TEKS Number and
Operations—K.2.B
Also K.2.F, K.2.C
MATHEMATICAL PROCESSES
K.1.D, K.1.G

7.4 Count and Write 13 and 14

? **Essential Question**

How do you count and write 13 and 14 with words and numbers?

Explore

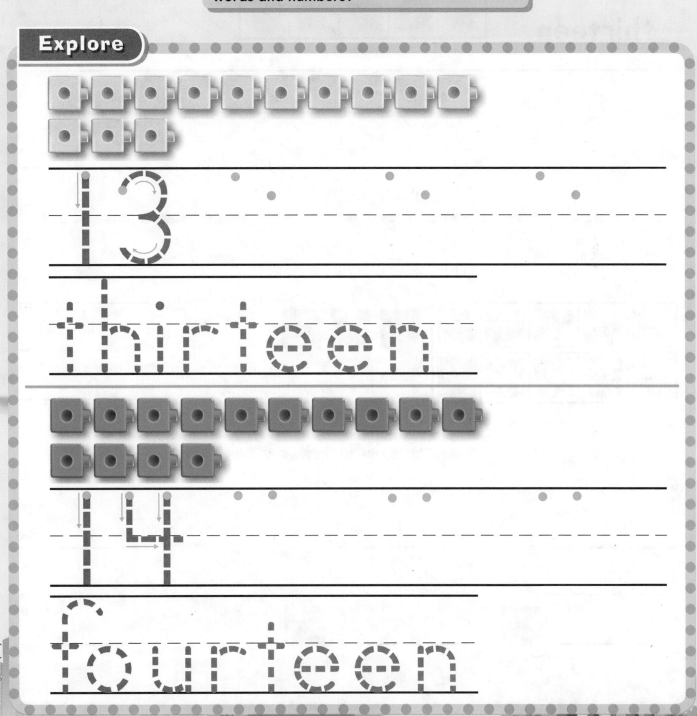

DIRECTIONS Count and tell how many. Trace and write the numbers and the words.

❶ ✔

13
thirteen

_____

- - - - - - - - - - - - - - -

_____

●●●●●●●●●●●●●●●●●●●●●●●●●●●●●●●●

 ②

_____

- - - - - - - -

_____

●●●●●●●●●●●●●●●●●●●●●●●●●●●●●●●●

③

_____   _____   _____

- - - - -   - - - - -   - - - - -

_____ ▪ _____ ▪ _____

●●●●●●●●●●●●●●●●●●●●●●●●●●●●●●●●

DIRECTIONS 1. Count and tell how many. Practice writing the number. **2.** Count and tell how many. Write the number. **3.** Look at the squares in Exercise 2. Write how many blue squares. Write how many red squares. Write how many squares in all.

Name _____

 4

14
fourteen

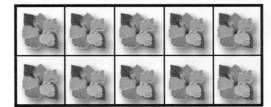

_____

- -

_____

 5

                                                    _____

                                                     - - - - - - - - - - - - - -

                                                    _____

 6

_____   _____   _____

- - - - - - -   - - - - - - -   - - - - - - -

_____   __________   _____

DIRECTIONS **4.** Count and tell how many.
Practice writing the number. **5.** Count and tell
many. Write the number. **6.** Look at the squares in
Exercise 5. Write how many red squares. Write how
many blue squares. Write how many squares in all.

 HOME ACTIVITY • Ask your child to
count and write the number for a set
of 13 or 14 objects, such as macaroni
pieces or buttons.

Problem Solving

7

13

8

14

Daily Assessment Task

9

_____

_ _ _ _ _ _

_____

DIRECTIONS **7.** Tia picked 13 purple flowers. Draw more purple flowers to show how many she picked. **8.** Calvin picked 14 red flowers. Draw more red flowers to show how many he picked. **9.** Count the cubes. Write the number.

7.4 Count and Write 13 and 14

1

13
thirteen

2

14
fourteen

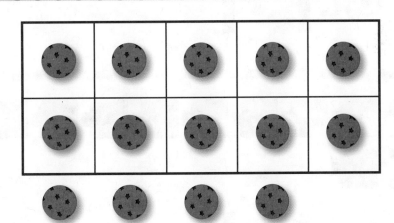

DIRECTIONS 1-2. Count and tell how many. Practice writing the number.

Module 7

two hundred twenty-one **221**

Lesson Check

TEXAS Test Prep

3

○ 13 ○ 14

4

○ 14 ○ 13

5

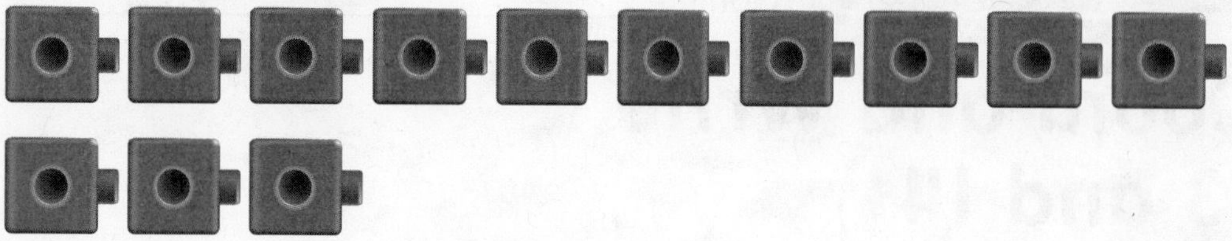

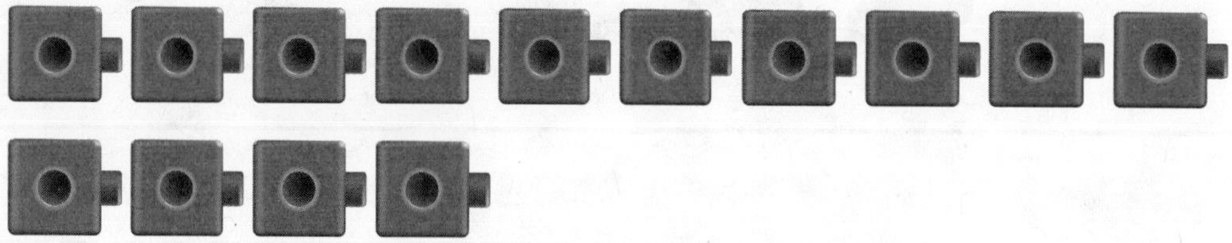

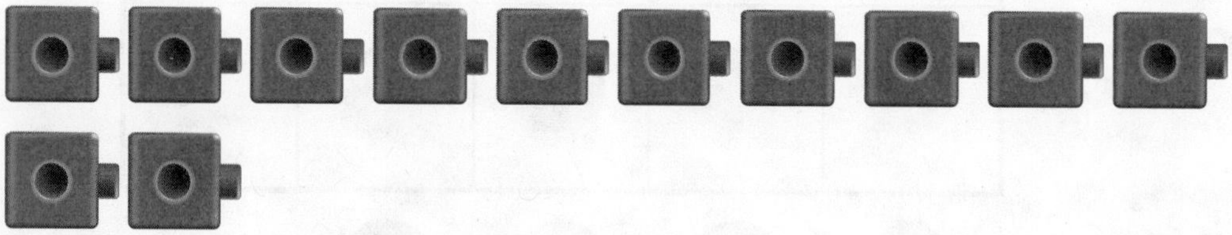

○ 14 ○ 12

DIRECTIONS Choose the correct answer. **3–5.** Count the cubes. How do you write that number?

TEKS Number and
Operations—K.2.B
Also K.2.A, K.2.C
MATHEMATICAL PROCESSES
K.1.D, K.1.G

7.5
HANDS ON

Model, Count, and Write 15

? Essential Question How do you write 15 and use objects to show 15 as ten and some more?

Explore

15

fifteen

DIRECTIONS Use counters to show the number 15. Draw the counters. Trace and write the number. Trace the word.

1 ✔

15
fifteen

_____

— — — — — — —

_____

 2

3 _____   _____

— — — — — — —   — — — — — — —

_____   **and**   _____

DIRECTIONS **1.** Count and tell how many. Write the number.   **2.** Use counters
to show the number 15. Draw the counters.   **3.** Look at the counters you drew. How
many are in the ten frame? Write the number. How many more? Write the number.

4

15
fifteen

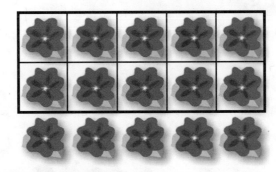

_____

– – – – – – – – – –

_____

5

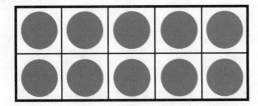   

_____

– – – – – – – – – –

_____

6

_____   _____   _____

– – – – – –   – – – – – –   – – – – – –

_____   _____   _____

DIRECTIONS **4–5.** Count and tell how many. Write the number. **6.** Look at the ten circles and some more in Exercise 5. Write how many blue circles. Write how many red circles. Write how many in all.

HOME ACTIVITY • Have your child use two different kinds of objects to show all the ways he or she can make 15, such as 8 pieces of macaroni and 7 pieces of bowtie pasta.

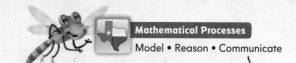

Mathematical Processes
Model • Reason • Communicate

Problem Solving

 7

Daily Assessment Task

 8

○ 15

○ 5

DIRECTIONS **7.** Start with the blue bead on the left. Circle to show 15 beads on the bead string. **8.** Choose the correct answer. Count the tickets. How many are there?

Name _____

7.5 HANDS ON
Model, Count, and Write 15

 1

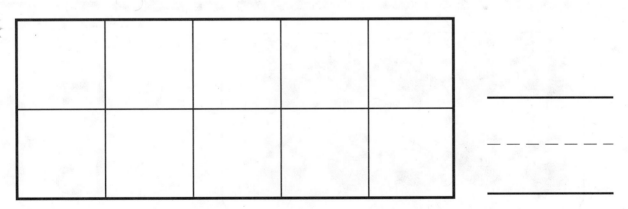

DIRECTIONS **1.** Draw counters to show 15. Write the number. **2.** Draw counters to show 14. Write the number.

© Houghton Mifflin Harcourt Publishing Company

3

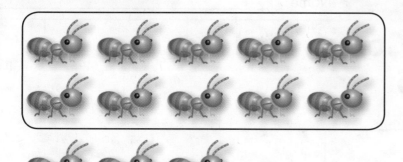

○ **3**

○ **13**

4

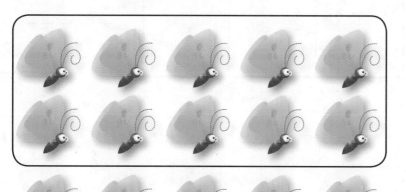

○ **15**

○ **5**

5

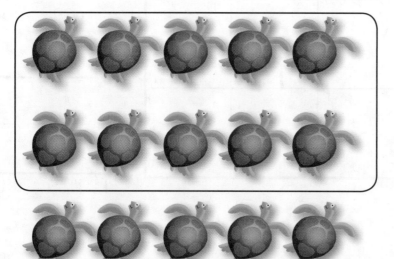

○ **14**

○ **15**

DIRECTIONS Choose the correct answer.
3. Count the ants. How many are there?
4. Count the butterflies. How many are there?
5. Count the turtles. How many are there?

TEKS Number and
Operations—K.2.F
MATHEMATICAL PROCESSES
K.1.E, K.1.D

7.6 PROBLEM SOLVING • One More and One Less

? Essential Question How do you draw a picture to find a number that is one more or one less?

🔑 Unlock the Problem

_____

- - - - - - -

_____ **children**

DIRECTIONS There are 14 children in the classroom. One more child walks into the classroom. How many children are in the classroom now? Draw to solve the problem. Write the number.

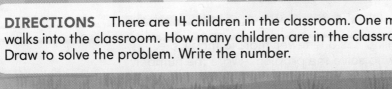

_____
- - - - - - -
_____ **marbles**

DIRECTIONS   1. Cole has 13 marbles. Phillip has one fewer marble than Cole. How many marbles does Phillip have? Draw to solve the problem. Write the number.

Share and Show

_____
- - - - - - -
_____ **children**

DIRECTIONS   2. There are 12 children in the drink line. The snack line has one more child than the drink line. How many children are in the snack line? Draw to solve the problem. Write the number.

HOME ACTIVITY • Use drawing paper to have your child draw pictures of one more or one less than any number 1 to 15.

        ○   ○

○ **14**   ○ **12**

DAILY ASSESSMENT TASK **3.** Choose the correct answer.
The bakery has 13 muffins. Which set shows a number one less than 13?
4. Choose the correct answer. There are 13 red cubes.
What number is one more?

7.6 HANDS ON

PROBLEM SOLVING • One More and One Less

1

_____
- - - - - - -
_____ **dogs**

DIRECTIONS **1.** There are 15 dogs playing at the dog park. One dog goes home. How many dogs are playing at the dog park now? Draw to solve the problem. Write the number.

②

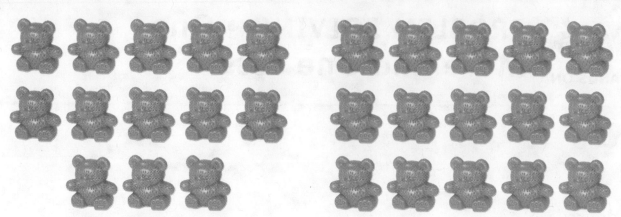

                ○   ○

③

      ○ **11**   ○ **10**

DIRECTIONS Choose the correct answer.
2. Lisa has 14 bear counters. Which set shows a number one more than 14? **3.** There are 12 red cubes. What number is one less?

Module 7 Assessment

Concepts and Skills

_____

- - - - - - - - - - - - - -

_____

_____

- - - - - - - - - - - - - -

_____

_____

- - - - - - - - - - - - - -

_____

_____

- - - - - - - - - - - - - -

_____

DIRECTIONS 1–4. Count and tell how many. Write the number.  TEKS K.2.B

5

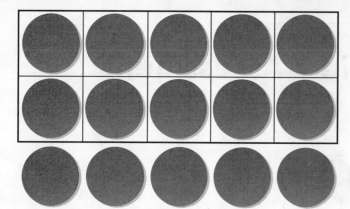

_____

- - - - - - - - -

_____

6

13

_____

- - - - - - - - -

_____

7

11

_____

- - - - - - - - -

_____

8

11

_____

- - - - - - - - -

_____

---

9 ⭐ **TEXAS Test Prep**

15

_____

- - - - - - - - -

_____

DIRECTIONS   5. Count and tell how many. Write the number. ⬇️ TEKS K.2.B
6–7. Write the number that is one more.   **8–9.** Write the number that is one
less. ⬇️ TEKS K.2.F

236 two hundred thirty-six

8.1
HANDS ON

Model and Count 16 and 17

TEKS Number and Operations—K.2.B
Also K.2.A
MATHEMATICAL PROCESSES
K.1.E

? Essential Question

How can you use objects to show 16 and 17?

Explore

DIRECTIONS Use counters to show the number 16. Add more to show the number 17. Draw the counters.

1

16
sixteen

2 ✓

3

_____   _____

and

DIRECTIONS **1.** Circle 10 peaches. Tell how many more there are. **2.** Place counters in the ten frames to show the number 16. Draw the counters. **3.** Look at the counters you drew in the ten frames. How many ones are in the top ten frame? Write the number. How many ones are in the bottom ten frame? Write the number.

17
seventeen

_____   _____

- - - - - - - - - - - - - - - - - - -

and

_____   _____

DIRECTIONS **4.** Circle 10 peaches. Tell how many more there are. **5.** Place and draw counters in the ten frames to show the number 17. **6.** Look at the ten frames. Write the number of ones in the top ten frame. Write the number of ones in the bottom ten frame.

HOME ACTIVITY • Draw two ten frames. Have your child use small objects to show the numbers 16 and 17.

Module 8 • Lesson 1

two hundred thirty-nine **239**

Problem Solving

7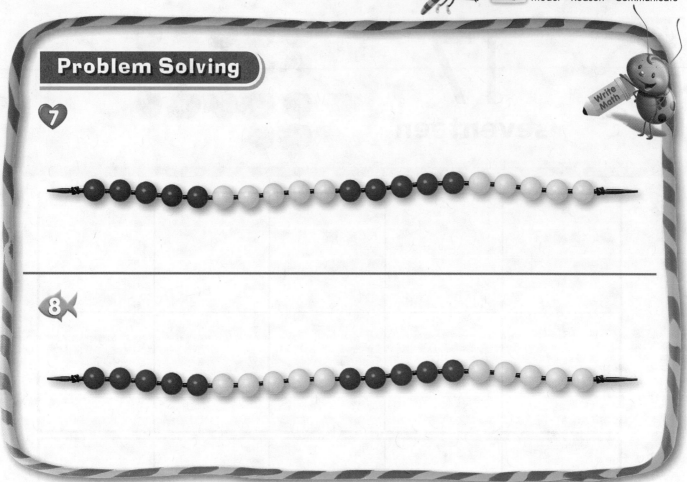

8

Daily Assessment Task

9

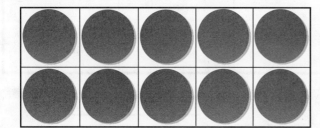 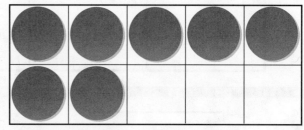

○ 16   ○ 17

DIRECTIONS **7.** Start with the blue bead on the left. Circle to show
16 beads on the bead string. **8.** Start with the blue bead on the left.
Circle to show 17 beads on the bead string. **9.** Choose the correct answer.
What number does the model show?

240 two hundred forty

Name _____

8.1
HANDS ON

Model and Count 16 and 17

1

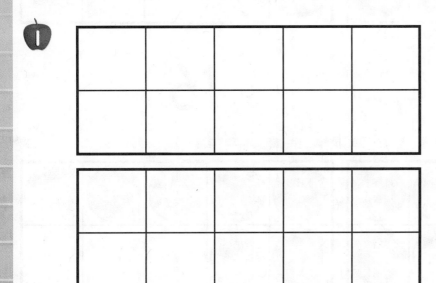

_____

- - - - - - - - - - -

_____

2

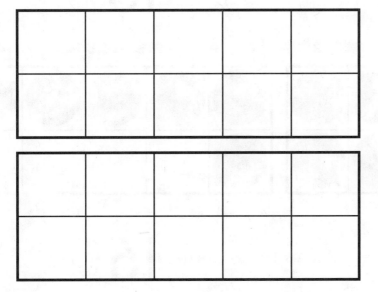

_____

- - - - - - - - - - -

_____

DIRECTIONS **1.** Draw counters to show 16. Write the number. **2.** Draw counters to show 17. Write the number.

3

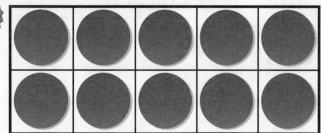   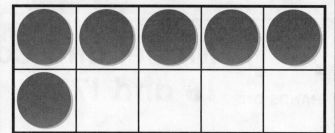

○ 17   ○ 16

4

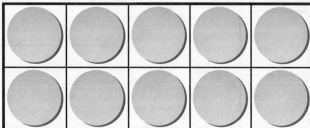   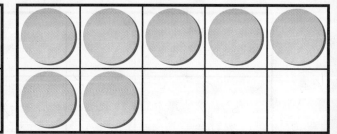

○ 17   ○ 16

5

   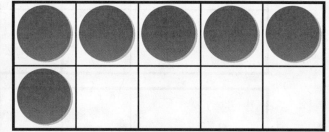

○ 15   ○ 16

DIRECTIONS Choose the correct answer.
3–5. What number does the model show?

Name _____

8.2 Count and Write 16 and 17

Essential Question

How can you count and write 16 and 17 with words and numbers?

Explore

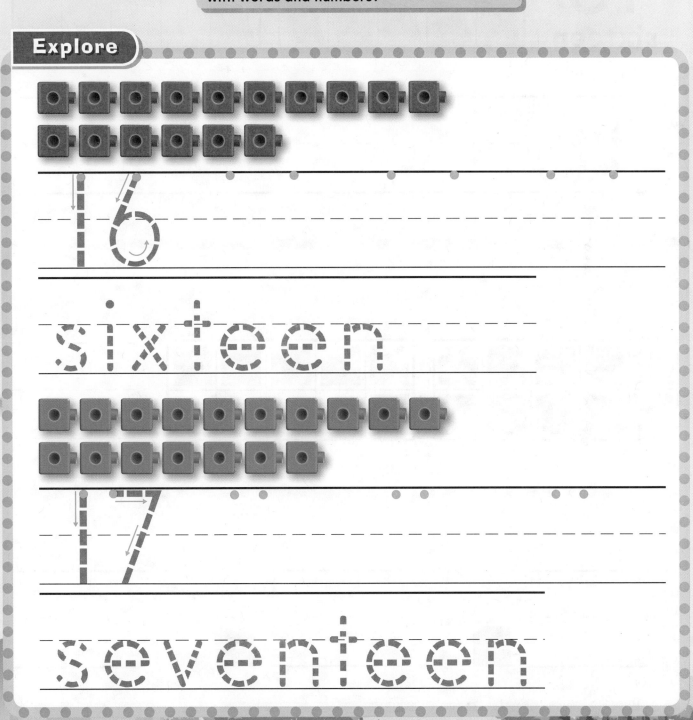

16

sixteen

17

seventeen

DIRECTIONS Count and tell how many. Trace and write the numbers and the words.

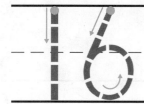

16
sixteen

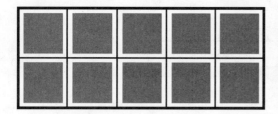

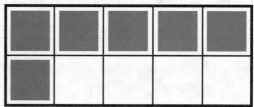

DIRECTIONS **I.** Count and tell how many. Practice writing the numbers. **2.** Count and tell how many. Write the number. **3.** Look at the ten frames in Exercise 2. Write how many red squares. Write how many blue squares. Write how many in all.

244 two hundred forty-four

4

17
seventeen

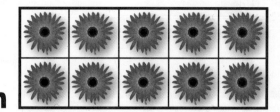

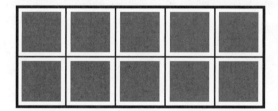

5

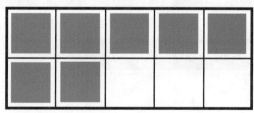

_____ _____

6 _____   _____   _____

- - - - -   - - - - -   - - - - -

_____    _____   _____

DIRECTIONS   4. Count and tell how many.
Practice writing the numbers.   **5.** Count and tell
how many. Write the number.   **6.** Look at the ten
frames in Exercise 5. Write how many red squares.
Write how many blue squares. Write how many in all.

HOME ACTIVITY • Ask your child to
count and write the number for a set
of 16 or 17 objects, such as macaroni
pieces or buttons.

Module 8 • Lesson 2

Problem Solving Real World

7

17
18
19

8

_____

- - - - - -

_____

Daily Assessment Task

9

_____

- - - - - -

10 and _____ 17

∘ 7   ∘ 17

DIRECTIONS **7.** Circle a number. Draw more flowers to show that number. **8.** Draw a set of 16 objects. Circle 10 of the objects. How many more objects are there? Write the number. **9.** Choose the correct answer. What number goes in the blank to make 17?

246 two hundred forty-six

Name _____

8.2 Count and Write
16 and 17

1

16
sixteen

16

2

17
seventeen

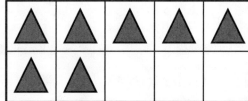

17

Module 8

DIRECTIONS 1–2. Count and tell how many. Write the numbers.

Lesson Check

TEXAS Test Prep

3

10 and ________ 16

○ 16 ○ 6

4

10 and ________ 17

○ 7 ○ 17

5

10 and ________ 15

○ 15 ○ 5

DIRECTIONS **3–5.** Choose the correct answer. What number goes in the blank?

TEKS Number and Operations—K.2.B
Also K.2.A
MATHEMATICAL PROCESSES
K.1.E

8.3
HANDS ON

Model and Count 18 and 19

? Essential Question

How can you use objects to show 18 and 19 as ten and some more?

Explore

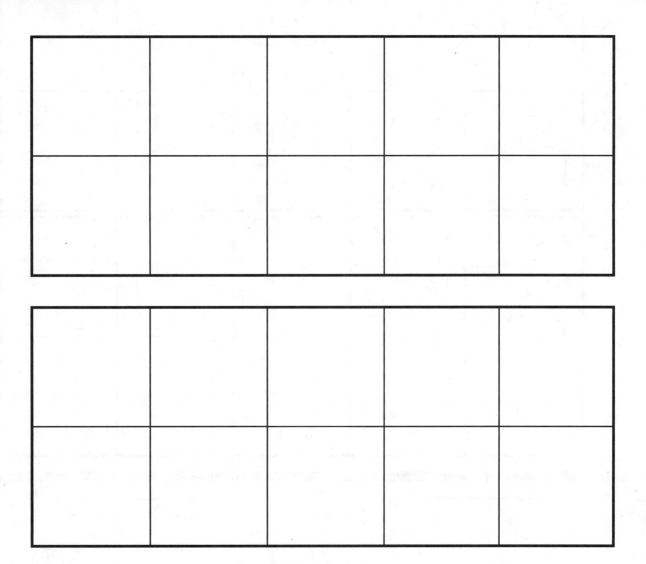

DIRECTIONS Use counters to show the number 18. Add more to show the number 19. Draw the counters.

① 🍎 # 18
eighteen

②✓

③ _____ _____

_____ **and** _____

DIRECTIONS **1.** Circle 10 peaches. Tell how many more there are. **2.** Place counters in the ten frames to show the number 18. Draw the counters. **3.** Look at the counters you drew in the ten frames. How many ones are in the top ten frame? Write the number. How many ones are in the bottom ten frame? Write the number.

19
nineteen

_____   _____

and

DIRECTIONS **4.** Circle 10 pears. **5.** Place and draw counters in the ten frames to show the number 19. **6.** Write the number in each ten frame.

HOME ACTIVITY • Draw two ten frames on a sheet of paper. Have your child use small objects to model the numbers 18 and 19.

Module 8 • Lesson 3

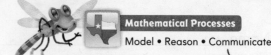

Mathematical Processes
Model • Reason • Communicate

Problem Solving

7

8

Daily Assessment Task

9

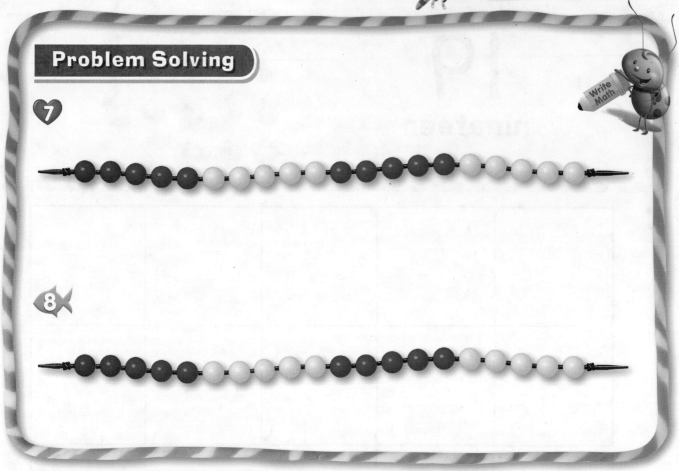

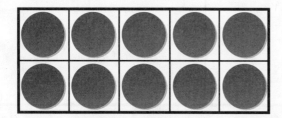 ○ 18

 ○ 17

DIRECTIONS **7.** Start with the blue bead on the left. Circle to show 18 beads on the bead string. **8.** Start with the blue bead on the left. Circle to show 19 beads on the bead string. **9.** Choose the correct answer. What number does the model show?

252 two hundred fifty-two

© Houghton Mifflin Harcourt Publishing Company

TEKS Number and Operations—K.2.B
Also K.2.A
MATHEMATICAL PROCESSES K.1.E

Homework and Practice

Name _____

8.3 HANDS ON Model and Count 18 and 19

1

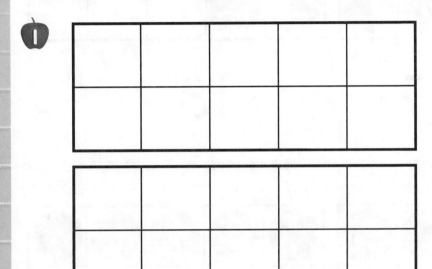

_____
- - - - - - - -
_____

2

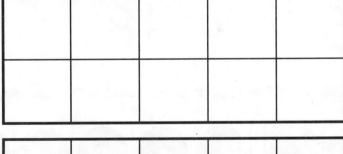

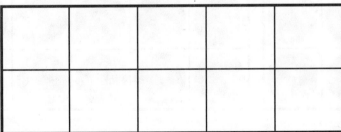

_____
- - - - - - - -
_____

DIRECTIONS **1.** Draw counters to show 18.
Write the number. **2.** Draw counters to show 19.
Write the number.

Module 8

two hundred fifty-three **253**

Lesson Check

 ⭐ **TEXAS Test Prep**

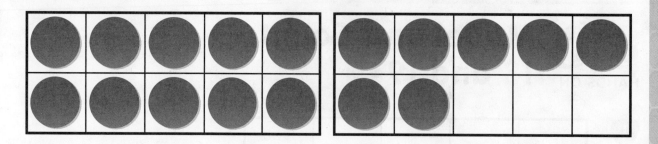

○ 17   ○ 18

○ 16   ○ 18

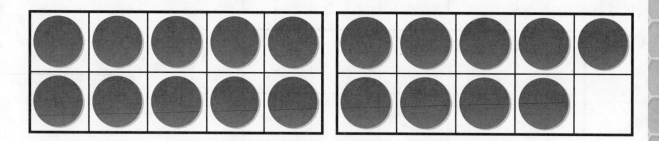

○ 18   ○ 19

254 two hundred fifty-four

DIRECTIONS Choose the correct answer.
3–5. What number does the model show?

Name _____

 8.4 # Count and Write 18 and 19

? Essential Question How can you count and write 18 and 19 with words and numbers?

Explore

18

eighteen

19

nineteen

DIRECTIONS Count and tell how many. Trace and write the numbers and the words.

1

18
eighteen

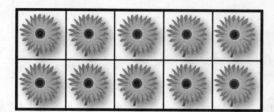
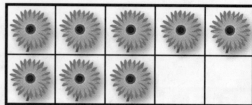

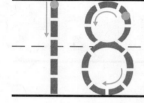

2 ✓

3

DIRECTIONS **1.** Count and tell how many. Practice writing the numbers. **2.** Count and tell how many. Write the number. **3.** Look at the ten frames in Exercise 2. Write how many green squares. Write how many blue squares. Write how many in all.

4

19
nineteen

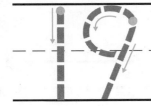

5

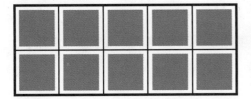

6

© Houghton Mifflin Harcourt Publishing Company

DIRECTIONS **4.** Count and tell how many. Practice writing the numbers. **5.** Count and tell how many. Write the number. **6.** Look at the ten frames in Exercise 5. Write how many blue squares. Write how many red squares. Write how many in all.

HOME ACTIVITY • Ask your child to count and write the number for a set of 18 or 19 objects, such as macaroni pieces or buttons.

Problem Solving *Real World*

7

🌺🌺🌺🌺🌺🌺🌺🌺🌺🌺

🌼🌼🌼🌼🌼🌼🌼🌼

_____

- - - - - -

_____

8

_____

- - - - - -

_____

Daily Assessment Task

_____
- - - - - -
_____

10 and ____ 18

∘ 18   ∘ 8

DIRECTIONS **7.** Jonah has 10 purple flowers. Kaiya has 8 red flowers. How many flowers do they have in all? Write the number. **8.** Draw a set of 19 objects. Circle 10 of the objects. How many more objects are there? Write the number. **9.** Choose the correct answer. What number goes in the blank?

8.4 Count and Write 18 and 19

1

18
eighteen

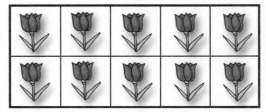 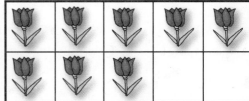

18

2

19
nineteen

19

Module 8

DIRECTIONS 1–2. Count and tell how many.
Write the numbers.

two hundred fifty-nine 259

Lesson Check

★ TEXAS Test Prep

3

10 and ______ 19

○ 19   ○ 9

4

10 and ______ 18

○ 8   ○ 18

5

10 and ______ 17

○ 17   ○ 7

DIRECTIONS **3–5.** Choose the correct answer. What number goes in the blank?

TEKS Number and
Operations—K.2.B
Also K.2.D

MATHEMATICAL PROCESSES
K.1.E

8.5 Model, Count, and Write 20
HANDS ON

? Essential Question

How can you show, count, and write 20 objects?

Explore

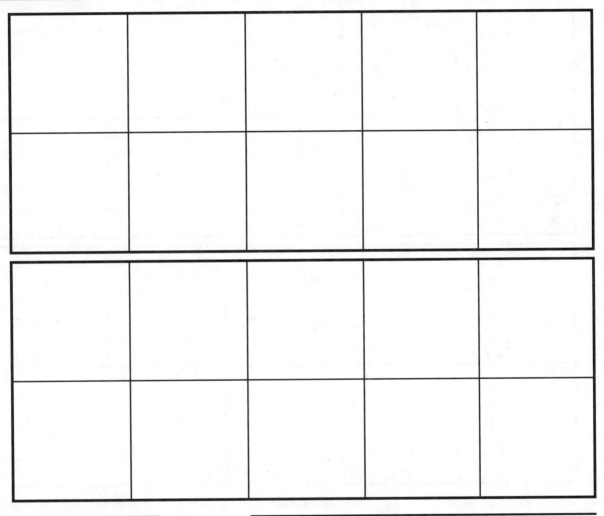

DIRECTIONS Use cubes to model 20. Draw the cubes.
Trace the number and word.

1 **20**

twenty

_____

- - - - - - - - -

_____

2

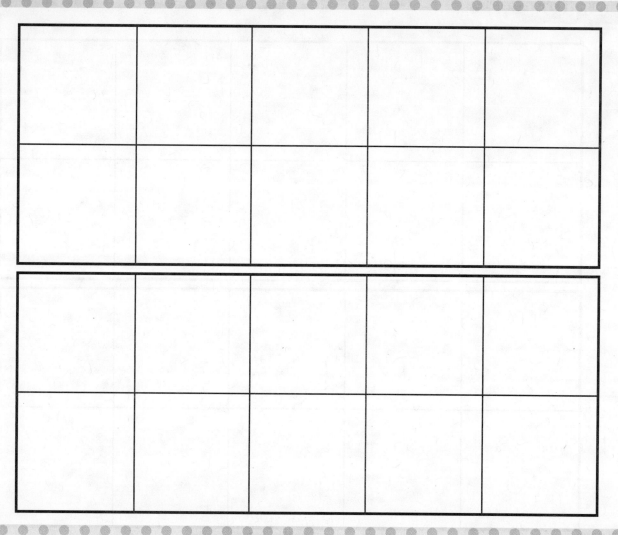

3

DIRECTIONS I. Count and tell how many. Write the number. **2.** Use cubes to model the number 20. Draw the cubes. **3.** Use the cubes from Exercise 2 to model ten-cube trains. Draw the cube trains.

Name _____

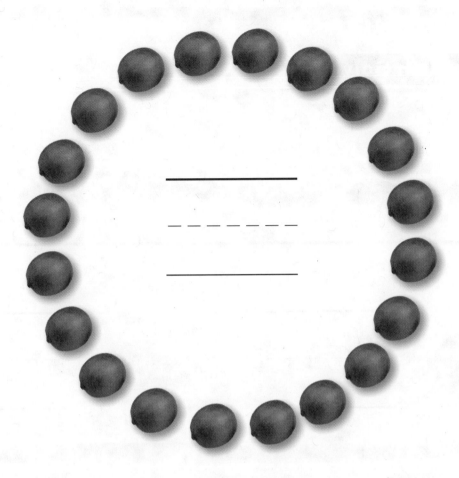

_____

- - - - - - - - -

_____

5

_____

- - - - - - - - -

_____

DIRECTIONS 4–5. Count and tell how many pieces of fruit. Write the number. Tell a friend how you counted the fruit.

HOME ACTIVITY • Draw two ten frames on a sheet of paper. Have your child show the number 20 by placing small objects, such as buttons or dried beans, in the ten frames.

Problem Solving

6

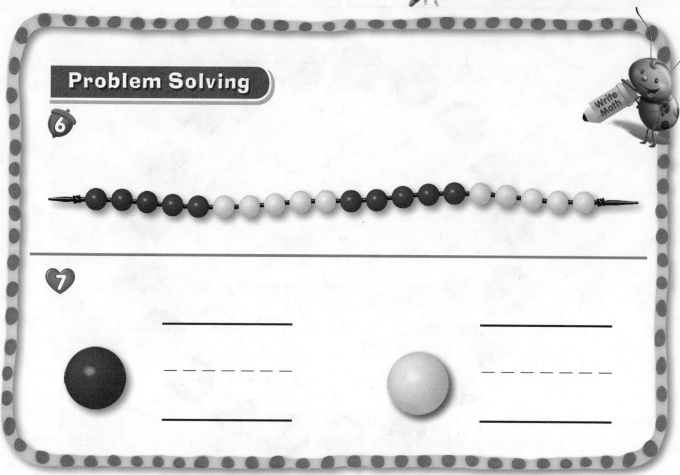

7

_____   _____

- - - - - - - - -   - - - - - - - - -

_____   _____

Daily Assessment Task

8

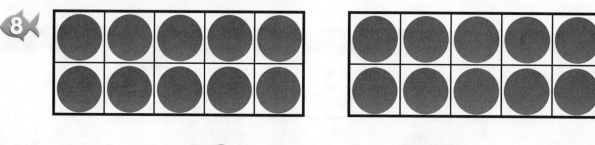

10   20

○   ○

DIRECTIONS **6.** Circle to show 20 beads. **7.** How many of each color bead did you circle? Write the numbers. Tell a friend about the number of each color bead. **8.** Choose the correct answer. What number does the model show?

TEKS Number and Operations—K.2.B
Also K.2.D
MATHEMATICAL PROCESSES K.1.E

Name _____

8.5
HANDS ON

Model, Count, and Write 20

1

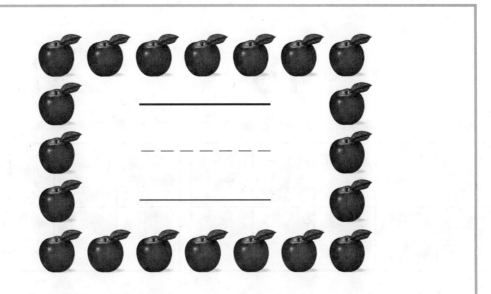

_____

- - - - - - - - -

_____

2

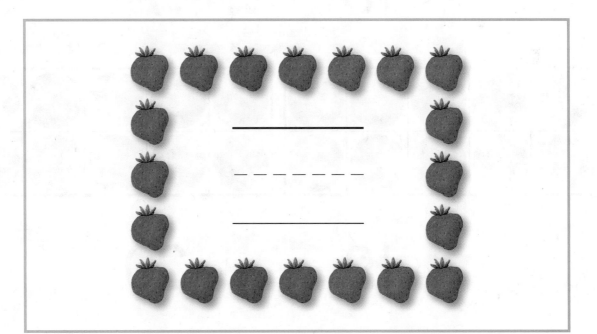

_____

- - - - - - - - -

_____

DIRECTIONS **1–2.** Count and tell how many pieces of fruit. Write the number. Tell how you counted the fruit.

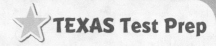
3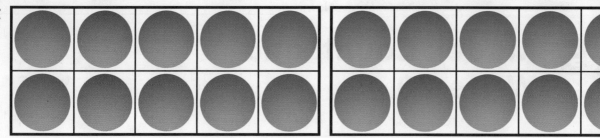

○ **18**   ○ **20**

4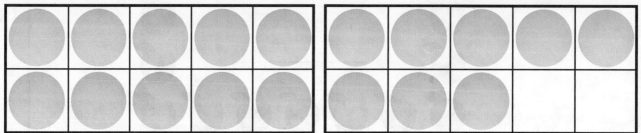

○ **18**   ○ **17**

5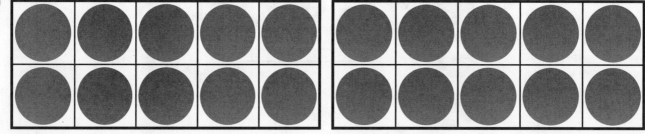

○ **19**   ○ **20**

DIRECTIONS Choose the correct answer.
3–5. What number does the model show?

TEKS Number and
Operations—K.2.C
Also K.2.A, K.2.B
MATHEMATICAL PROCESSES
K.1.E

8.6 Count and Order to 20

? Essential Question

How can you count forward to 20 from a given number?

Explore

Hands On

```
1  2  3  4  5  6  7  8  9  10  11  12  13  14  15  16  17  18  19  20
```

DIRECTIONS Place counters in the ten frames as you count from 1 to 20. Now start with 20. Remove counters from the ten frames as you count backward from 20.

Module 8

two hundred sixty-seven **267**

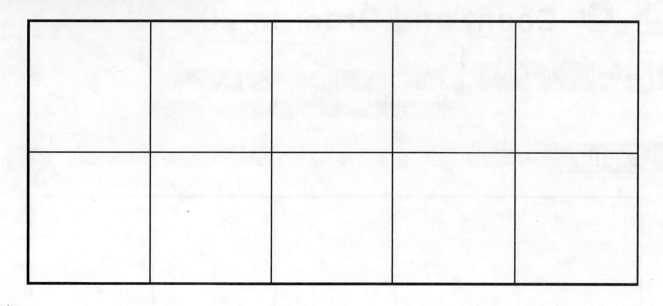

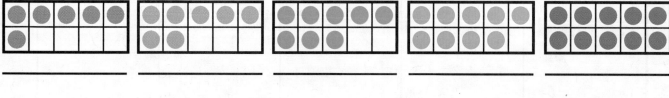

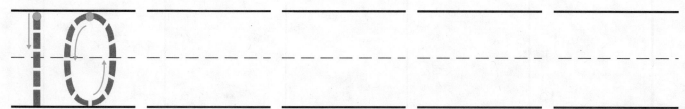

DIRECTIONS **I.** Place counters in the ten frame to model each number as shown. Write the number as you count forward. **2.** Now start with 10. Remove counters from the ten frame as you count backward. Trace and write the number as you count backward.

268 two hundred sixty-eight

Name _____

3

4

DIRECTIONS 3. Place counters in the ten frame to model each number as shown. **4.** Write the number as you count forward. Now start with 20. Remove counters from the ten frame as you count backward.

HOME ACTIVITY • Have your child count a set of objects up to 20 and tell how many.

Module 8 • Lesson 6

Problem Solving

5

11	___	13	14	___
16	17	___	19	20

Daily Assessment Task

6

17	18	___	20

17
○

19
○

DIRECTIONS 5. Write to show the numbers in order. Count forward
to 20. **6.** Choose the correct answer. What is the missing number?

270 two hundred seventy

Name _____

8.6 Count and Order to 20

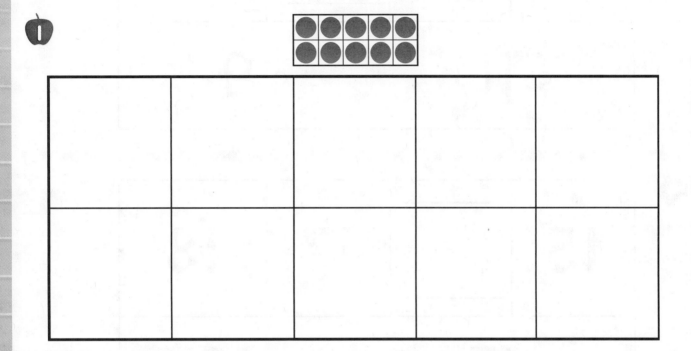

1

2

20

DIRECTIONS **1.** Place counters in the ten frames as you count forward from 11 to 20. **2.** Now start with 20. Remove counters from the ten frame as you count backward to 11. Trace and write the number as you count backward from 20.

Module 8

two hundred seventy-one **271**

3

9	10	_ _ _ _	12

    ○ 11   ○ 9

4

15	_ _ _ _	17	18

    ○ 17   ○ 16

5

17	_ _ _ _	19	20

    ○ 18   ○ 20

DIRECTIONS Choose the correct answer.
3–5. What is the missing number?

TEKS Number and
Operations—K.2.F
Also K.2.E, K.2.G
MATHEMATICAL PROCESSES
K.1.D

8.7 One More and One Less

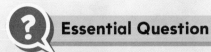

? Essential Question

How do you find the number that is one more or one less than a given number?

Explore

Hands On

10

DIRECTIONS Place 10 counters in the ten frame. Take one counter away. Write the number that is one less than 10. Place 10 new counters in the ten frame. Add one more counter. Write the number that is one more than 10.

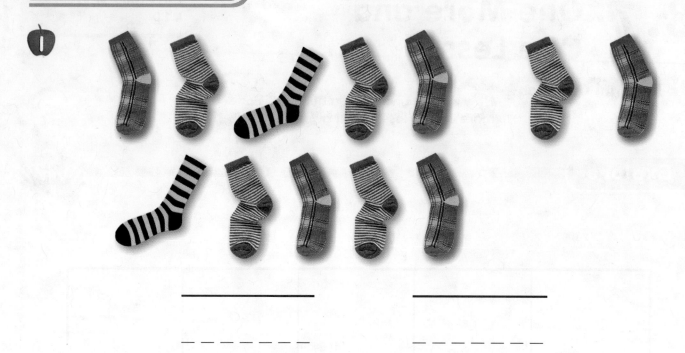

_____   _____
- - - - - - - - -   - - - - - - - - -
_____   _____

_____   _____
- - - - - - - - -   - - - - - - - - -
_____   _____

DIRECTIONS **I.** There are 12 socks. Write the number that is one more than 12. Write the number that is one less than 12. **2.** There are 15 hats. Write the number that is one more than 15. Write the number that is one less than 15.

3

17

_____   _____

- - - - - - - -   - - - - - - - -

_____   _____

4 ✓

14

_____   _____

- - - - - - - -   - - - - - - - -

_____   _____

5

19

_____   _____

- - - - - - - -   - - - - - - - -

_____   _____

DIRECTIONS **3–5.** Look at the number. Write the number that is one less. Write the number that is one more.

 HOME ACTIVITY • Show your child a set of 11 to 20 objects such as spoons or forks. Have your child create a set of objects that shows one more or one less.

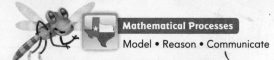

Mathematical Processes
Model • Reason • Communicate

Problem Solving Real World

6

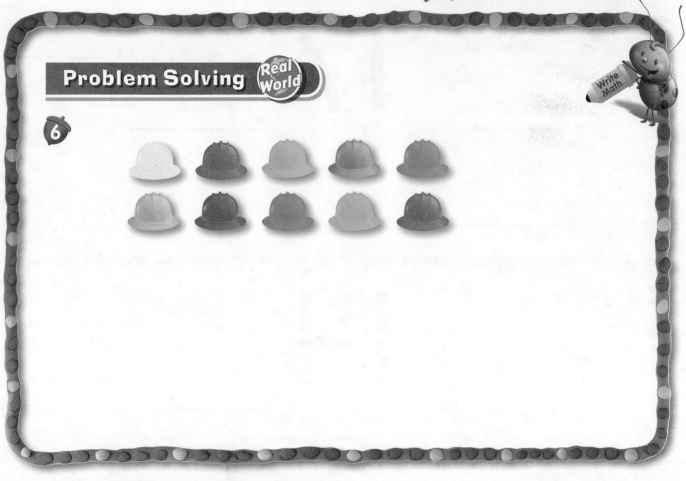

Daily Assessment Task

7

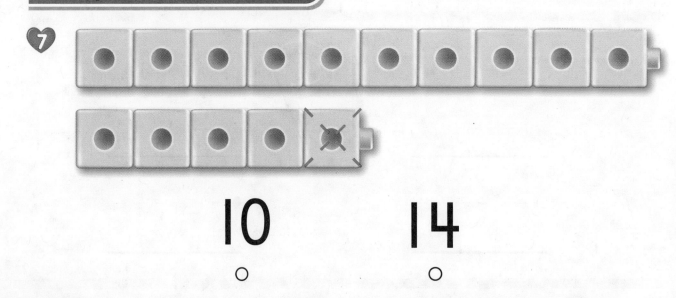

10
○

14
○

DIRECTIONS **6.** Adele has 10 hats. Seamus has one more hat than Adele. Draw to show how many hats Seamus has. **7.** Choose the correct answer. There are 15 cubes. What number is one less?

276 two hundred seventy-six

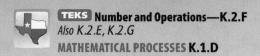
Name _____

_____   **19**   _____

_____   **16**   _____

3

_____   **18**   _____

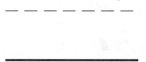

DIRECTIONS **1–3.** Look at the number. Write the number that is one less. Write the number that is one more.

4

○ 15   ○ 17

5

○ 10   ○ 12

6

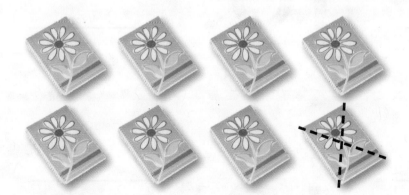

○ 7   ○ 9

DIRECTIONS Choose the correct answer.
4. There are 16 cubes. What number is one less?
5. There are 11 stars. What number is one more?
6. There are 8 books. What number is one less?

TEKS Number and Operations—K.2.H
Also, K.2.B
MATHEMATICAL PROCESSES
K.1.A, K.1.B

8.8 PROBLEM SOLVING • Compare Numbers to 20

? Essential Question

How can you solve problems using the strategy make a model?

♀ Unlock the Problem

Hands On

DIRECTIONS Alison has more than 15 yellow cubes. Josh has fewer than 17 yellow cubes. Show the cubes, or select an *i*Tool. Compare the sets of cubes. Draw the sets. Tell a friend about your drawing.

DIRECTIONS **1.** Kaelin has 18 apples. Chase has two fewer apples than Kaelin. Use cubes, or select an *i*Tool, to model the sets of apples. Compare the sets. Which set is larger? Draw the sets. Write how many in each set. Circle the greater number. Tell a friend how you compared the numbers.

Name _____

_____
- - - - - - - - -
_____

_____
- - - - - - - - -
_____

DIRECTIONS **2.** Skyler has 19 oranges. Taylor has two fewer oranges than Skyler. Use cubes, or select an *i*Tool, to model the sets of oranges. Compare the sets. Which set is smaller? Draw the sets. Write how many in each set. Circle the number that is less. Tell a friend how you compared the numbers.

HOME ACTIVITY • Have your child count two sets of objects in your home, and write how many are in each set. Then have him or her circle the greater number. Repeat with sets of different numbers.

3

○ **10**

○ **11**

4

○ **16**

○ **17**

5

17   **20**

○   ○

DIRECTIONS Choose the correct answer. **3.** How many balloons are there? **4.** How many blocks are there? **5.** Which number is greater?

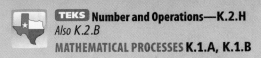
Homework and Practice

Name _____

8.8 PROBLEM SOLVING • Compare Numbers to 20

1

_____

- - - - - - - - - -

_____

_____

- - - - - - - - - -

_____

DIRECTIONS **I.** Pat has 20 crayons. Alan has two fewer crayons than Pat. Draw the sets of crayons, or select an *i*Tool to show the sets. Compare the sets. Which set is larger? Write how many in each set. Circle the greater number. Tell a friend how you compared the numbers.

○ **12**

○ **14**

○ **16**

○ **18**

14   **15**

○   ○

DIRECTIONS Choose the correct answer.
2. There are 13 pumpkins. What number is one more than 13? **3.** There are 17 ears of corn. What number is one less than 17? **4.** Which number is greater?

✓ **Module 8 Assessment**

Concepts and Skills

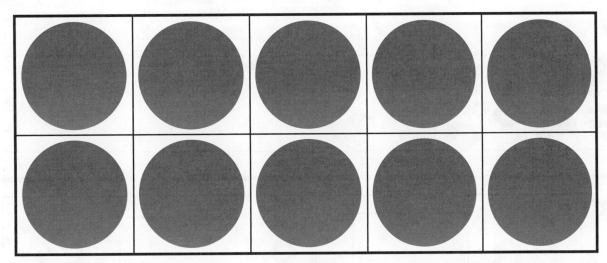

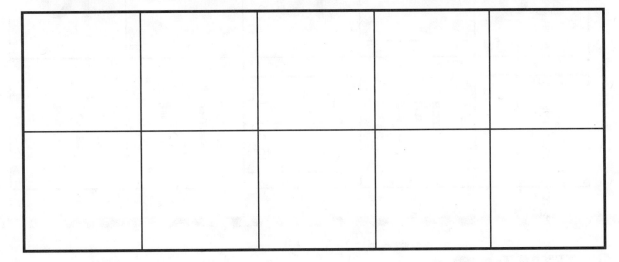

10 and ‾‾‾‾‾ _ _ _ _ _

‾‾‾‾‾ _ _ _ _ _

DIRECTIONS 1. Draw counters to show 16. Write the number of counters you drew. Write the number of counters in all. ◆ TEKS K.2.B

_____

③

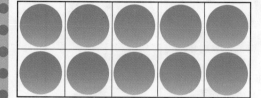
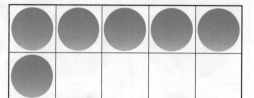

_____

④

20	——— - - - ———	18	——— - - - ———	16
——— - - - ———	14	——— - - - ———	12	11

⭐ **TEXAS Test Prep**

○ 16   ○ 14

DIRECTIONS **2–3.** Write the number. TEKS K.2.B **4.** Begin with 20. Write the number as you count backward from 20. TEKS K.2.C **5.** Choose the correct answer. Which number is one less than 15? TEKS K.2.F

Name _____

  Unit I Assessment

1

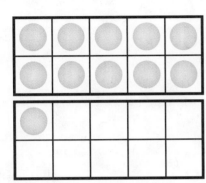 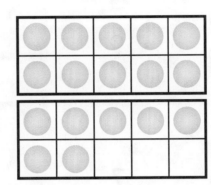 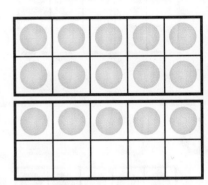

fifteen   eleven   seventeen

Concepts and Skills

 2

 _____

•••

3

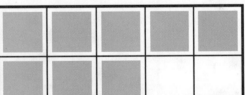

15   _____ _____ _____ _____   20

•••

DIRECTIONS I. Draw lines to match the counters in the ten frames to the number word.
2. Count and tell how many. Write the number. ⬇ TEKS K.2.B **3.** Start with I5. Count forward. Write
the numbers in order. ⬇ TEKS K.2.B

5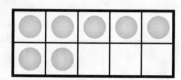

      5   7

      ○   ○

6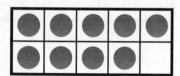

      7   9

      ○   ○

7

8

      ○   ○

8   11 12 10   14 15 16

             ○   ○

DIRECTIONS **4.** Draw more flowers to show 14 flowers. ⬥ TEKS K.2.G **5–6.** Mark under the number that shows how many. ⬥ TEKS K.2.B **7.** Mark under the set that models the number at the beginning of the row. ⬥ TEKS K.2.G **8.** Mark under the numbers that show them in order. ⬥ TEKS K.2.A

9

14

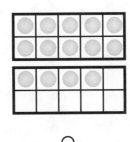
○

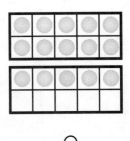
○

10

17   19

○   ○

11

○ 10

○ 8

12

15

○ 14

○ 16

DIRECTIONS **9.** Mark under the set that shows the number at the beginning of the row.
✦ TEKS K.2.B   **10.** Mark under the number that shows how many.   ✦ TEKS K.2.G   **11.** Mark beside the number that is one more.   ✦ TEKS K.2.F   **12.** Mark beside the number that is one less.   ✦ TEKS K.2.F

Performance Task

_____   _____   _____

- - - - - - -   - - - - - - -   - - - - - - -

_____   _____   _____

PERFORMANCE TASK   This task will assess the child's understanding
of identifying and ordering numbers to 20.   TEKS K.1.G, K.2.A, K.2.B, K.2.F

add sumar

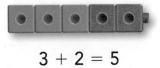

3 + 2 = 5

alike igual

and y

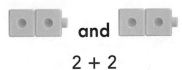

and

2 + 2

big grande

big

capacity capacidad

Capacity is how much something can hold.

category categoría

fruits

toys

circle círculo

classify clasificar

apples

not apples

color color

red | **blue** | **yellow**
rojo | azul | amarillo

green | orange
verde | anaranjado

compare comparar

cone cono

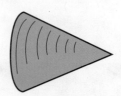

corner esquina

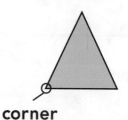

corner

count backward contar hacia atrás

5, 4, 3, 2, 1

count forward contar hacia adelante

1, 2, 3, 4, 5

cube cubo

curved curva

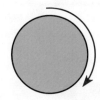

The edge of a circle is **curved**.

curved surface
superficie curva

Some solids have a **curved surface**.

cylinder cilindro

different diferente

dime moneda de diez centavos

earn ganar

You **earn** income when you work.

eight ocho

eighteen dieciocho

eleven once

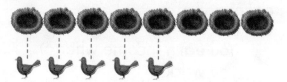

fewer menos

fewer birds

fifteen quince

fifty cincuenta

1	2	3	4	5	6	7	8	9	10
11	12	13	14	15	16	17	18	19	20
21	22	23	24	25	26	27	28	29	30
31	32	33	34	35	36	37	38	39	40
41	42	43	44	45	46	47	48	49	50

five cinco

five frame cuadro de cinco

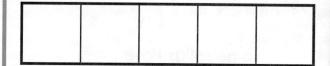

flat plano

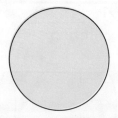

A circle is a **flat** shape.

flat surface superficie plana

Some solids have a **flat surface**.

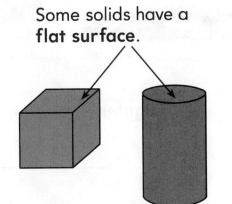

four cuatro

fourteen catorce

graph gráfica

row
fila

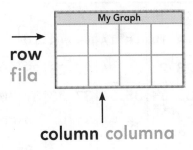

column columna

greater mayor

9 is **greater** than 6

heavier más pesado

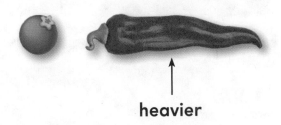

heavier

hundred chart tabla con los números hasta el 100

1	2	3	4	5	6	7	8	9	10
11	12	13	14	15	16	17	18	19	20
21	22	23	24	25	26	27	28	29	30
31	32	33	34	35	36	37	38	39	40
41	42	43	44	45	46	47	48	49	50
51	52	53	54	55	56	57	58	59	60
61	62	63	64	65	66	67	68	69	70
71	72	73	74	75	76	77	78	79	80
81	82	83	84	85	86	87	88	89	90
91	92	93	94	95	96	97	98	99	100

is equal to es igual a

$$3 + 2 = 5$$

3 + 2 **is equal to** 5

less menor/menos

9 is **less** than 11

9

11

lighter más liviano

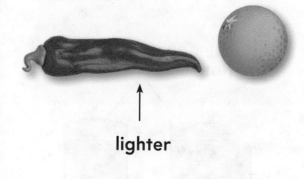

lighter

longer más largo

longer

match emparejar

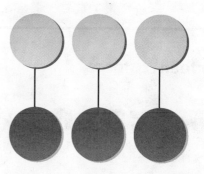

minus – menos

4 – 3 = 1

4 **minus** 3 is equal to 1

more más

more leaves

nickel moneda de cinco centavas

nine nueve

nineteen diecinueve

one uno

one hundred cien

1	2	3	4	5	6	7	8	9	10
11	12	13	14	15	16	17	18	19	20
21	22	23	24	25	26	27	28	29	30
31	32	33	34	35	36	37	38	39	40
41	42	43	44	45	46	47	48	49	50
51	52	53	54	55	56	57	58	59	60
61	62	63	64	65	66	67	68	69	70
71	72	73	74	75	76	77	78	79	80
81	82	83	84	85	86	87	88	89	90
91	92	93	94	95	96	97	98	99	100

order orden

The numbers are in **order** from 1 to 5.

1, 2, 3, 4, 5

pairs pares

number **pairs** for 3

3 and 0
2 and 1
1 and 2
0 and 3

penny moneda de un centavo

picture graph gráfica de dibujos

Red and Blue Cubes			
○			
○	○		

plus + más

2 **plus** 1 is equal to 3
2 + 1 = 3

quarter moneda de veinticinco centavos

real-object graph gráfica de objetos reales

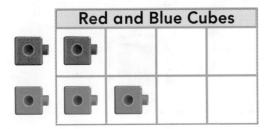

Red and Blue Cubes			

rectangle rectángulo

same height de la misma altura

same length del mismo largo

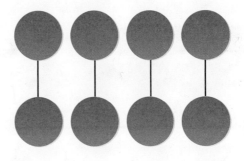

same number el mismo número

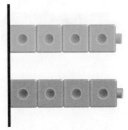

same weight del mismo peso

seven siete

seventeen diecisiete

shape forma

shorter más corto

side lado

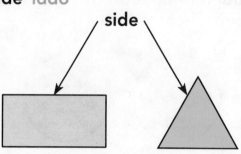

sides of equal length lados del mismo largo

six seis

sixteen dieciséis

size tamaño

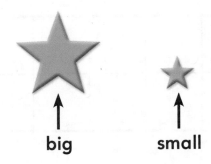

big   small

sort clasificar

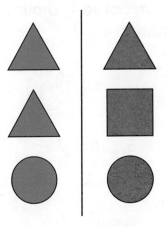

small pequeño

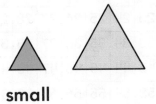

small

sphere esfera

solid sólido

solid

A **cylinder** is a solid shape.

square cuadrado

subtract restar

Subtract to find out how
many are left.

$$3 - 1 = 2$$

ten frame cuadro de diez

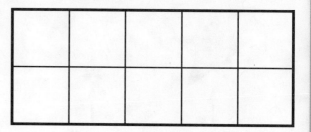

taller más alto

taller

tens decenas

1	2	3	4	5	6	7	8	9	10
11	12	13	14	15	16	17	18	19	20
21	22	23	24	25	26	27	28	29	30
31	32	33	34	35	36	37	38	39	40
41	42	43	44	45	46	47	48	49	50
51	52	53	54	55	56	57	58	59	60
61	62	63	64	65	66	67	68	69	70
71	72	73	74	75	76	77	78	79	80
81	82	83	84	85	86	87	88	89	90
91	92	93	94	95	96	97	98	99	100

↑
tens

ten diez

thirteen trece

three tres

---

three-dimensional shapes
figuras tridimensionales

---

triangle triángulo

---

twelve doce

twenty veinte

---

two dos

---

two-dimensional shapes
figuras bidimensionales

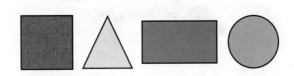

---

vertex vértice

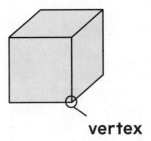

vertex

vertices vértices

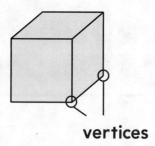

vertices

weight peso

zero, none cero, ninguno

zero fish